"Tell me and I forget. Teach me and I remember. Involve me and I learn."

-BENJAMIN FRANKLIN

Developed by the Northeast Entrepreneur Fund, Inc.

Helping your business succeed

CORE FOUR® Business Planning Course

Copyright 1998, 2000, 2003, 2004, 2005, 2006, 2007
Northeast Entrepreneur Fund, Inc.

ISBN: 0–9746127–0–7

Acknowledgements
We would like to acknowledge Suzanne Cunningham and Barbara J. Meyers, who led the development of the original curriculum. We would also like to acknowledge Stephen C. Peterson, Sr., Myrna Ahlgren, Alison Beauregard, Jane Bymark, Kelly Cooke, Mary M. Cossalter, Siiri Gilness, John Larson, Paul LaSalle, Susan Martin, Mary Mathews, Dale Porter, Anita Provinzino, Brenda Shoberg, Robert Voss, and Shawn Wellnitz for their contributions to the current curriculum.

Printed in the United States of America.
Second Printing.

Greetings.

Whether you are opening this workbook as part of a CORE FOUR® Business Planning Course or as a self-study guide, you will learn to plan a business that meets your personal and professional goals.

The CORE FOUR® Business Planning Course will teach you, as an aspiring or existing business owner, the information and skills you need in four fundamental or "CORE" elements of business planning:

- Plan for business success
- Plan your business to meet the needs of the marketplace
- Plan for your business' cash flow needs
- Plan how your business will operate

Starting with a business idea, use CORE FOUR® Business Planning Course to plan a business in real time. As you learn by doing, you will see the business idea evolve as you build the details. While it is true that some individuals have been successful without a business plan, our experience demonstrates that a strong, well-researched business plan increases the likelihood of success. You will save time and money later on by making mistakes up front and on paper. The skills you learn in business planning will pay off in other areas of your life, as well.

After you have planned your business, your CORE FOUR® instructor can guide you to resources that will help you finance and operate your business.

The Northeast Entrepreneur Fund developed the CORE FOUR® Business Planning Course in 1998 as a culmination of 10 years of teaching entrepreneurs to plan businesses. The Entrepreneur Fund started in 1989, at a time when the economy in northeastern Minnesota was weak. We live and work in a rural region of the United States. Our economy, based in natural resources, does not have a history of entrepreneurship. We have relied on business ownership outside the region and government to provide jobs and economic solutions.

The Entrepreneur Fund was started to provide a supportive resource with training, technical assistance, and financing for people–residents of the region-with ideas for businesses that could replace their lost jobs. Initially we provided training and technical assistance one-on-one. As the numbers grew we began offering workshops to groups of people. Adding one topic at a time, the collective effort of Entrepreneur Fund staff resulted in the CORE FOUR® Business Planning Course.

We wish you success in your business and in achieving your personal and professional goals!

Mary Mathews
President, Northeast Entrepreneur Fund, Inc.

INTRODUCTION

WHAT IS THE CORE FOUR® BUSINESS PLANNING COURSE?

The CORE FOUR® Business Planning Course is a course that teaches strategies in how to plan a business. It focuses on certain core business planning tools and concepts for planning any business; however, it is not a small business management course.

The four core bodies of knowledge that a business owner must have in order to operate a successful business include a clear understanding of the following: the marketplace and how it works, how to manage cash, how to get things done as well as do things, and how to stay focused on a clear set of personal and business goals.

CORE FOUR® Business Planning Course presents the tools of knowledge for how to build a business plan. With this knowledge, you will begin the process of gathering the information you need to plan your business. Your experience and continued learning provide ongoing business development tools and information. Once you have the knowledge of how to plan a business, you can use this knowledge for any business idea, at any time, for the rest of your life.

WHAT ARE THE FOUR CORES?

Planning strategies for each of the four cores are presented in separate sections of this workbook. Page numbers reflect the specific section.

Core 1: Success Planning – Success Planning presents tools for: self-assessment, financial goal setting, boundary setting, communication skills, selling skills, and contingency planning. You will prepare your "business owner" resume and personal financial plan. Success Planning is also threaded throughout the course with instruction and exercises for teaching you about due diligence, raising your self-awareness about your wants and needs, the business wants and needs, your role in the business, business ethics, and business legitimacy.

Core 2: Market Planning – Market Planning presents tools and strategies for transforming your dream into a reality of a market-driven business including: identifying customers, analyzing competition and industry, identifying a market niche and position, options for distributing products and services, identifying features and benefits of products and services, image and packaging decisions, promotional planning, pricing, selling, and contingency planning. Market Planning stresses the importance of focusing on matching the business owner's dream with the needs and wants of customers, and interacting in a competitive marketplace.

Core 3: Cash Flow Planning – Cash Flow Planning presents detailed strategies for preparing a cash flow projection, projecting sales, setting goals, and contingency planning. It focuses on helping you understand that the business and the person are separate economic entities. Cash Flow Planning helps clarify personal financial needs from the financial needs of the business.

Core 4: Operations Planning – Operations Planning presents key issues and strategies for having a legitimate business, compliance with all legal requirements, and effective business operations. It helps identify what work must be done, how all of the work will be done, and who will do the work. Operations Planning helps you identify the various "hats" you, the business owner, must wear and how to stay focused.

CORE FOUR® COURSE DEVELOPMENT AND HISTORY

The Northeast Entrepreneur Fund has developed programs such as the CORE FOUR® Business Planning Course based on customer needs. Thousands of prospective and existing business owners have come to us and asked the hard questions, made the tough choices, and shared their lessons learned. Bankers, venture capitalists, and other lenders have offered feedback by critiquing the business plans that were produced by students of the CORE FOUR® Business Planning Course. In order to provide quality, comprehensive business planning training, the Entrepreneur Fund continues to enhance and customize its training programs.

Created in 1989, The Northeast Entrepreneur Fund is a private, not-for-profit, full-service microenterprise development business that serves 11 rural counties in northeastern Minnesota and northwestern Wisconsin. The Northeast Entrepreneur Fund was presented with the 1998 Presidential Microenterprise Award for Excellence in Developing Entrepreneurial Skills. With a mission to help people become economically self-sustaining through self-employment (owning and operating their own businesses), the Entrepreneur Fund strives to focus on the critical needs of small business owners with the intent of helping small businesses thrive, not just survive. With dollars (loans) and human capital (training and consulting), the Entrepreneur Fund has helped start, stabilize, or expand hundreds of small businesses and has exceeded $6.5 million in loans (as of July 2007) to small businesses.

Every customer who has taken this course has done so either because they wanted to start a business, or because they wanted to operate an existing business in a better way. They have come into the class with a desire to learn how to create a comprehensive and realistic business plan, and to apply this knowledge to a real business project in real time.

It took a decade to hone this training curriculum to the four cores presented herein, and the dedicated staff at the Entrepreneur Fund is passionate about these cores. Entrepreneur Fund staff are all involved in some way in coaching and counseling small business owners and in making decisions on whether or not to lend money to someone who typically does not have sufficient collateral or who does not have perfect credit. All of the business development and training staff at the Northeast Entrepreneur Fund have either owned or managed a small business. They have all contributed to the development of this course.

WHY IS CORE FOUR® BUSINESS PLANNING COURSE BEING OFFERED NATIONALLY?

Distribution of this course beyond northeastern Minnesota and northwestern Wisconsin is market-driven based on requests from Northeast Entrepreneur Fund peers and colleagues in the field of microenterprise development.

The Northeast Entrepreneur Fund is a member of the Association for Enterprise Opportunity (AEO), the national trade association for microenterprise development organizations. Other technical assistance professionals within the microenterprise development industry, most of whom are members of AEO, are continually seeking the best tools that will be most helpful to their customers.

The success of the customers of the Northeast Entrepreneur Fund (80% business startup survival rate as compared to national 80% business startup failure rate), along with the reputation of the CORE FOUR® Business Planning Course, has motivated other organizations to want this curriculum for their customers.

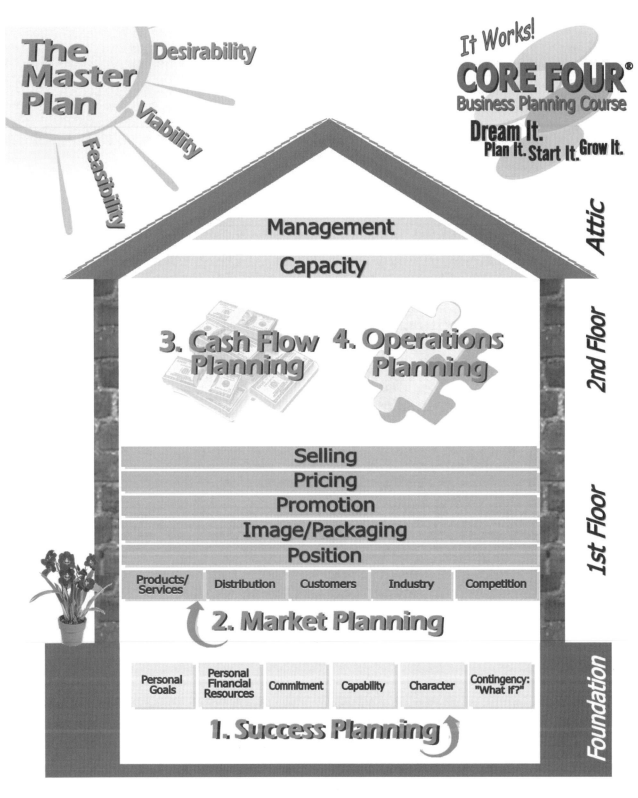

The Master Plan

Desirability

Viability

Feasibility

It Works!

CORE FOUR®
Business Planning Course

Dream It.
Plan It. Start It. Grow It.

Attic

Management

Capacity

2nd Floor

3. Cash Flow Planning

4. Operations Planning

1st Floor

Selling

Pricing

Promotion

Image/Packaging

Position

| Products/ Services | Distribution | Customers | Industry | Competition |

2. Market Planning

Foundation

| Personal Goals | Personal Financial Resources | Commitment | Capability | Character | Contingency: "What If?" |

1. Success Planning

www.corefouronline.com
1-800-422-0374

Business Plan Blueprint

SUCCESS PLANNING

C O N T E N T S

I AM AN ENTREPRENEUR:

I am authorized
to make all of the decisions in my business.

I am responsible
for learning what I need to learn, and for
all outcomes of my decisions.

I am accountable
for the success of my business.

DEFINE YOUR BUSINESS – YOUR DREAM

The difference between fantasy and reality is disappointment.

Many businesses fail because the owners fantasized about their business and went into it wishing and hoping for success. They started a journey with no destination in mind and, when they got "anywhere," were disappointed because they ended up "nowhere."

Without goals, a fantasy remains a fantasy. Setting goals will help transform fantasy into reality. Knowing where you want to go and what you want to do when you get there will help you prepare for your journey.

Believing it will happen is the first step toward making it happen.

Visualize what will happen. Start by outlining your business idea – your dream.

Just like designing and building your dream house, building a business is based on your vision of what your dream business will be. And, like building your dream house, building a business has fundamental planning strategies for you to use to be sure that the end result is as close to your vision as it can realistically be.

HOW DO YOU DEFINE YOUR BUSINESS?

Visualize how your ideal business will look when you "open the door." Answer the following questions. General answers, ideas and guesses are fine. This is your first written snapshot of your dream.

1. **What are your products or services?**

    _____

    _____

    _____

    _____

2. **Who are your customers?**

    _____

    _____

    _____

    _____

3. **Where is your business located?**

    _____

    _____

    _____

    _____

4. **What does the location look like?**

    _____

    _____

    _____

    _____

5. **How many employees are working? Who are they? What are they doing?**

    _____

    _____

    _____

    _____

6. **What is your role in the business?**

    _____

    _____

    _____

    _____

7. Do you like what you will be doing? Why?

_____

_____

_____

_____

8. How do you see the business in two years? Have you expanded? Hired employees? Moved? Added new product lines?

_____

_____

_____

_____

9. Two years later, is your role what you thought it would be when you started the business? Do you like it? Is it right for you?

_____

_____

_____

_____

10. Why do you want to do this business?

_____

_____

_____

_____

11. What do you personally want to achieve?

_____

_____

_____

_____

12. What goals do you have for your business?

_____

_____

_____

* * * * *

The CORE FOUR® Business Planning Course provides you with planning tools you can use to build your business; to transform it from a dream to a reality.

When you have completed this course and worked on your business plan using these tools, it will be interesting for you to revisit your answers to the above questions.

CASE STUDY

What a wonderful adventure you are embarking on! Congratulations! You are about to learn the difference between achieving your dream and experiencing your worst nightmare.

As a case study, let's look at a nightmare first...

THE NIGHTMARE: MIKE THE MECHANIC

Note: Mike the Mechanic is completely fictional. Any resemblance to actual persons is purely coincidental. Mike is a composite of a number of small business owners.

Mike worked as a mechanic for 15 years at a large automobile dealership in a small midwestern town. The owner liked Mike and entrusted him with a great deal of authority. Everyone in town knew Mike. His work was high quality. He was fast. He always made a quick diagnosis of the problem and made practical, reasonably priced repairs. He had a reputation for being able to figure out tough problems that other mechanics couldn't fix.

The owner retired and sold the dealership to his son-in-law and nephew. The new owners were people that Mike couldn't stand. They were bossy and ordered him around. They tried to force him to comply with repair standards and schedules, and wanted him to do and sell more services than customers needed.

Many of his customers, after listening to Mike complain about his job, told Mike, "You should start your own business. You would have more work than you can handle." After about six months of gnashing his teeth, Mike decided it was time to cut loose. He started his own automotive service garage.

Mike had some acreage out in the country, about 11 miles from town. He quit his job. He built a large pole building, using some savings and taking out a second mortgage on his property. He purchased new equipment and tools. He painted a sign on a piece of plywood and hung it from his mailbox at the end of his gravel driveway. He placed a small ad in the local newspaper.

Prior to leaving his job, Mike told a number of his customers about how unhappy he was with the new owners and that he was starting his own business. He gave them his home phone number.

Some months later, Nancy Wagner, a long-time customer of Mike's, noticed her car wasn't running properly. She had heard that Mike had started his own business. She didn't know Mike's last name. When she called the dealership to find Mike, they were rude and told her they didn't know anything about where he had gone. Nancy asked some of her neighbors and co-workers about Mike, and finally found someone who knew his phone number.

Nancy called Mike's number. A child answered the phone. When Nancy asked if Mike was available, the child responded, "DAAAAAD," by shouting into the telephone. Nancy heard a "clunk," some dogs barking, a baby crying, and the noise from a television or radio. Some minutes later, a man's gruff voice said, "Yeah."

"Mike?" asked Nancy. "Yeah," he responded. Nancy introduced herself and explained that her car was making a clunking noise. She asked if Mike could work on her car. Mike said, "Well, got one up on the hoist now, waiting for parts. Got another out in the yard waiting for the hoist." Nancy, unsure of what this meant, asked again, "Can you work on my car, and if so, when?" Mike mumbled to himself, then finally told Nancy to bring it out on Thursday morning.

Nancy asked for directions, which were: go west on the main highway for 7 miles, then south on the gravel county road for 2 miles, then west on another gravel county road for 2 miles to the first driveway on the left. "You'll see the sign," Mike said.

Nancy made arrangements with a friend to follow her out to Mike's. On a rainy April Thursday, she and her friend began the journey. She found the first gravel road, missed the second because there was no road sign, backtracked 3 miles, guessed at which road to take, drove 2 miles and saw no sign for Mike's garage. Backtracking again, she finally saw a mailbox with a small wooden sign. Pulling up to the sign, she read, "Mike's Garage."

She pulled into the driveway. After heavy rains, it had turned into two muddy ruts. The driveway was about ½ mile long. Her friend in the car behind her was skidding and swerving, trying to stay on the road.

They finally pulled into a yard. There was a white house on the right, badly in need of paint. There were several large outbuildings as well; a barn, what appeared to be a machinery shed, and another building. Two large dogs came running from the porch of the house, barking and growling. They leaped at Nancy's driver side window. They ran back and forth between the two cars, growling and leaping.

Terrified, Nancy drove right up to the house and honked her horn. A woman came out the front door. Nancy cracked her window and yelled, "Where's Mike?" The woman pointed to the machinery shed.

Nancy backed up and drove over to the machinery shed, where there was a large overhead door that was shut, and a smaller entrance door that was ajar. The dogs followed her and ran into the shed.

Nancy waited a minute or two. No one came from the shed. She honked her horn. After another minute Mike peeked out the door. Nancy rolled her window down slightly and said, "I'm afraid of your dogs."

By now the two dogs were leaping at Mike. He kicked one, hollered something, pushed them into the shed and disappeared. Moments later, he returned and said he had locked up the dogs.

Nancy got out of her car and explained to Mike that her car was making a "clunking" sound and that it squealed horribly when turning left. Mike stared at Nancy. Then he began explaining that he still had one car on the hoist and was waiting for parts. He complained that he had to pay C.O.D. for the parts and that they were going to be expensive. He complained to Nancy that if she needed parts she would have to pay up front so that he could get them faster. Nancy asked what parts Mike thought he would need and how much they would cost. Mike explained that he didn't know and wouldn't know until he could get the car up on the hoist.

Mike also explained to Nancy that while his parts prices were high, he had reduced his labor rate to half of what the competition was charging. He muttered that it was unfair that his vendors were "jerking him around."

Nancy asked when Mike would be able to get her car up on the hoist. Mike didn't know. He was waiting for parts. They were supposed to be there later that day. If they didn't come that day, they should come the next day, Friday. Nancy

asked, if he got the parts, how long he would have to work on the other car. Mike wasn't sure. Nancy asked if she could reschedule for another day. Mike wasn't sure.

Nancy thanked Mike for his time and signaled to her friend that they were leaving. Nancy got into her car and left. When she got back to town, she drove directly to the auto dealership, met with the service manager who scheduled her repairs for later that day, told her the car would be done at 4:00 pm, and asked her if she needed a loaner. Nancy said no, and got a ride to work from her friend. The whole ordeal had taken her two hours.

A few months later Mike sold his fishing boat so he could make a mortgage payment and pay some vendors. Another month later he sold his canoe and his four-wheeler so he could make another mortgage payment. A few weeks later he sold his interest in his hunting shack to one of his neighbors so that he could make another mortgage payment and buy more parts.

Mike finally cashed in his retirement fund from when he worked at the dealership. He paid some bills and bought a new piece of equipment.

Mike's banker called him several months later, explaining that Mike had been late with his mortgage payments and was now two months past due. Mike's vendors refused to sell him any parts. Mike's phone had been disconnected twice, and Mike had to pay past phone bills plus a reconnect fee (he used the money in his son's savings account). Mike's customers were refusing to pay their bills. One customer was suing Mike.

After about eight months, Mike filed bankruptcy and closed his business. His wife had taken their two children and moved in with her parents. The homestead was foreclosed on and eventually sold. Mike moved into a small trailer on a friend's farm. He told everyone he knew that starting your own business was a horrible idea, that bankers were all jerks, and that people just wanted to rip you off. He told everyone that his customers were a bunch of whiny idiots who were too cheap to even work with.

* * * *

Mike's business failed for a lot of tactical reasons that you will learn about in this course. Most importantly, Mike's business failed because he let other people make choices and decisions he should have been making.

Mike's vendors chose to not sell him any parts because Mike didn't pay them on time. Mike liquidated all of his assets to pay bills. Mike could have chosen to plan his cash flow more carefully. He should also have chosen when to stop. Mike chose to operate his business on his terms. He should have chosen to operate his business for his customers.

A business failure is when other people make your decisions for you because the decisions you have made were not in the best interest of your business.

Throughout this course, you will learn tools, techniques and strategies to help you understand your authority, accountability, and responsibility.

At the end of the course, you can review Mike's scenario, and think of how you would counsel Mike to prevent his ultimate business closure.

Keep Mike in the back of your mind as you go through your business planning process. Counsel yourself as though you were counseling Mike.

If you step back from your own interests and process to imagine that you are doing this as a consulting project for someone else, you maintain more objectivity about some of the tough choices you will be making.

As you go through Success Planning, you will set goals, look at your strengths and weaknesses, and begin planning. This process will help you understand business needs and hopefully avoid Mike's mistakes.

WHAT ARE THE CHARACTERISTICS OF A SUCCESSFUL BUSINESS OWNER?

The characteristics below describe those aspects of your character that will make the greatest contributions to your energy, endurance, and healthy decision-making when you own and operate a business.

CAPABLE *Able, skilled, competent, having the qualities necessary for owning and operating your own business.*	I've got experience and knowledge to get the job done. Where I need help, I get it. I've done things like this in the past.
COMMITTED *In charge, obligated, bound, and loyal to the business.*	I usually finish what I start. No matter what, I'm determined that this business is a success, and I'm willing to do what needs to be done.
CHARACTER *The nature, quality and behavior for performing the work of the business; moral strength; fortitude; reputation.*	I'm willing to listen and learn. I have the patience and fortitude to operate in the type of market environment that I will encounter. I'm comfortable perceiving myself selling and talking to customers, supervising employees, or negotiating with vendors.
CAPACITY *The time and tools required to perform the work of the business.*	I have the personal time, commitment, and resources I need to carry out the role I must play in the business.
COLLATERAL *Of corresponding value or importance, designated as security for payment of a debt or performance of a contract.*	I'm willing to pledge something of value to get the capital my business needs, and I am willing to risk losing what I pledge.
CREDIT WORTHINESS *Possessing the integrity and ability to meet payments. Having worth, value or merit.*	I've kept all of my past promises. My family, friends, and colleagues trust me. I deserve to be trusted by my customers, my lenders, my employees, my business partners, and my suppliers.
CONTINGENCY *The chance that something unexpected might happen or conditions may change.*	I'm prepared if something unforeseen happens. If this business idea doesn't work, I'll get a job or do what I have to do to support myself, and my family, and repay my debts.

KNOW THYSELF

How will you succeed in a business? Do you have a business now? How well do you know what your business needs from you and what you have to give to your business? What do your customers want or need from your business?

WHAT YOUR BUSINESS NEEDS

(some or all of the following):

Your commitment of time.

Your commitment of financial resources.

Your skill in managing financial resources.

Your experience in this business or industry.

Your commitment to a successful business.

Constant attention to the marketplace.

Selling skills.

Promotional skills.

Customer service.

Operating systems and procedures.

Record keeping and accounting.

Inventory management and control.

Production management.

Service management.

Performance measuring and monitoring.

Regular commitment of open hours.

Compliance with laws and regulations.

Compliance with tax filings and payments.

Employee management.

Insurance protection.

Problem solving.

New ideas.

To operate even if you are ill or have personal problems.

What else?

WHAT DO YOU HAVE TO MEET THESE NEEDS?

You are the key to the success of your business. If you don't have the skills or experience your business needs, what will you do about it? For example, your business needs record keeping and accounting. If you don't have the skill or interest, what will you do to make sure your business has these resources? And, what will the impact be on the business?

If you will be reliant on resources to help you start or grow your business, specifically lenders or investors, they will be committing to *you* and your opportunities to succeed.

CAPITALIZE ON YOUR STRENGTHS

If you have written a résumé in the past, you likely listed the jobs you've had, what your position was, and how long you had the job.

A "business owner" résumé goes in a different direction. Some of your life experiences that may have had nothing to do with a job may be more important to your success in business.

Joe has a job now – he is the head of a crew that resurfaces roadways. He's been doing this work for 23 years, and is thinking about early retirement. He wants to start a business that organizes youth in-line skate sporting tournaments. What experience does his road crew job bring to his business? How can he demonstrate his experience and knowledge in the youth sport competition industry?

Well, Joe had seven sons, the oldest is now 19 and the youngest is 12 (two sets of twins). In his history as a parent, he has thousands of hours of experience as a volunteer organizer, coach, promoter, and fan of the in-line skate sporting event industry. He has traveled all over the state and even to other states to help develop, promote, and set up in-line skate competitions. He's been doing this for 15 years.

Joe also has a home computer and a digital camera. As a hobby and to support the activities of his sons, he developed a web page. He takes pictures at sporting events and displays them on the web page so that other parents can see their kids "on the web." He has a calendar of events and occasionally writes "how to" articles for parents that he also posts on the web site. For a fee, he prints "collector cards" for parents that have their kid's picture and statistics on them.

Does it sound like Joe has a chance in this industry? If we didn't know about Joe's "personal" experience, what would his traditional résumé have told us?

"Whaddya mean I need to change my price-to-earnings ratio? Last month I booked 18 tournaments and brought in $43,000!"

Worksheet–Business Owner Résumé

On the next page, write your "business owner" résumé. Take an inventory of your life's work. Consider anything, even if you were a paper carrier in grade school. Revisit your life experiences, skills, education, hobbies and personal interests, and think about how they apply to the needs your business will have. When you are ready to include this résumé in your business plan, you can edit it to specifically address your market, operations, and financial plans.

Most important: what specific experience do you have working in the *industry or business that you are planning*? What has your role been?

Under what circumstances were you:

- Responsible for making decisions?
- Responsible for seeing that work was accomplished?
- Authorized to make decisions?
- Authorized to direct work or other activity?
- Accountable for the outcomes of an effort?

How can you demonstrate your problem solving skills and experience? How can you demonstrate your knowledge of the *specific marketplace that your business will be in*?

Use extra sheets if necessary

COMPENSATE FOR YOUR WEAKNESSES

You have opportunities to "fill the gaps" in your experience, skill or knowledge. You can take classes to learn about record keeping. You can get experience in your business or industry by volunteering or getting a job. You can "shadow" another business owner to learn about business operations. You can plan to hire people who have specific skills that you don't have.

On the worksheet below, write the ideas you have that will fill the gaps of experience or education you need to serve your business. Three example strategies are included in the worksheet. If you hire someone, what qualifications should they have? What choices or alternatives do you have? What will the impact be on the business? How much will it cost? How long will it take?

Worksheet–Professional Development Plan

Weakness:	Compensate by:
Record keeping and accounting	Contract for services with Acme Accounting. Monthly fee of $350 negotiated for first year, including setting up record keeping system.
Industry experience	Join trade association – first year membership fee $250. During business planning process, work with vendors and suppliers to learn about the industry.
Selling	Use business plan research to strengthen knowledge of your business. Practice your speech in front of a mirror.
	Take a class or seminar.
	Hire a salesperson.

WHAT DO YOU WANT YOUR BUSINESS TO DO FOR YOU?

It's interesting to ask people why they want to have their own business. Here are some typical responses:

I want to be my own boss.
I want to spend my time on my own terms.
I don't like working for someone else.
My product/service is the best there is.
I'm really good at what I do.
I want to work at home.
I want to spend more time with my family.
I don't work well as an employee.
I'm tired of helping other people get rich.
I want my kids to work in my business.
I want to work with my spouse/partner.

Rarely, if ever, do people say …

I WANT TO MAKE LOTS OF MONEY! I WANT TO BE RICH! RICH! RICH!

Any or all of the motives listed above are important. However, in order for your business to be successful, it *must* produce the financial return that you need.

WHAT IS A PERSONAL FINANCIAL GOAL?

Is it to be rich? Is it to pay all of your bills each month? How much money is enough? It varies for each person and business. From *Cheapskate Monthly*, January, 1995:

> "Seek solvency. Solvency simply means being comfortable with the money you have. Solvency is that confident feeling of being prepared for any circumstance, of living with joy and peace, of living within your means at all times."

HOW TO SET PERSONAL FINANCIAL GOALS

1. Think about your life and how you want to live it.

2. Identify the types and amounts of cash you will spend and *when* you will spend it.

3. Record the cash you will spend as *uses* on a personal cash flow form.

4. Identify the types and amounts of cash income you have access to and *when* you will receive it.

5. Record your cash income as *sources* of cash on a personal cash flow form.

6. Figure the difference between *sources* and *uses*.

7. If you have more *uses* than *sources*, you don't have enough cash to meet your needs. Consider life adjustments that may result in increasing your *sources* or decreasing your *uses*.

8. Take action to meet your goals.

OWNER DRAW

When you identify how much cash you need as "take home pay," this amount is called *owner draw*. This is the amount of cash you will draw from the business on a regular basis.

You and your business are *separate economic entities*. The cash in your business belongs to your business. The owner draw you take is for you to use to pay your personal expenses.

When you identify how much cash you need each year to live your personal life, divide the total by 12 (months) and prepare your annual budget, month-by-month. Plan to *draw the same amount every month* from your business to meet your personal needs.

If your business does not produce enough cash to provide you with the draw you need, you will not have the cash to meet your personal financial goals.

Owner draw should be recorded on your *personal* cash flow plan as a *source* of cash *for you*.

Owner draw should be recorded on your *business* cash flow as a *use* of cash *from your business*. It should be the *first cash flow assumption* you figure out, and *the first item recorded on your business cash flow*.

YOU GET PAID LAST

If the business can't pay you *after* everyone else (your vendors, lenders, employees and taxes) has been paid, both you and your business will suffer.

Who could you not pay? If you don't pay your vendors, you won't have inventory to sell. If you don't pay your lenders, they will foreclose on your debt. If you don't pay your employees, you will lose them and perhaps suffer legal hassles as well. If you don't pay your taxes, the taxing authority could close your business.

WHAT IS A BUSINESS FAILURE?

A business failure is when someone else, not the business owner, makes the choices:

The lender who forecloses on a debt, the landlord who sends an eviction notice, the employees who sue the employer for non-payment of wages, the taxing authority who closes a business and liquidates the assets, the vendor who refuses to sell to a business because the business doesn't pay their bills, the utility company who shuts off the power to a business because the bills aren't paid.

Owning your own business is an enriching experience on many levels. You have an opportunity to make more money than if you had a job. You have an opportunity to fulfill your goals for how you spend your time and what you do with your time.

On the other side of this coin, when you own your own business it is likely that you will work harder than you ever have before. If you *invest yourself* in your business with all of your time, commitment, passion, energy and financial risk, and do not receive enough money in return, the results can be devastating to you and your family. It is essential that you know when you have taken *enough* risk versus too little or too much risk.

When someone who is self-employed does not make enough money to personally survive, his or her decision-making skills go awry, and both the business and the person suffer financially.

Businesses close every day. Just because they close doesn't mean they failed. Many business owners made a choice to close their business, either because it wasn't generating enough cash and profits, or because the owner didn't want to operate the business any longer. These choices aren't failures, because the business owner made them. Tough business decisions include closing a business – *knowing when you have taken enough risk versus too little or too much risk.*

The worksheet on the following page is for you to use to take a snapshot of your net worth. What assets and liabilities do you have right now?

Worksheet—Personal Income and Expenses (Monthly)

What must your owner draw (your take-home pay) be in order for you to be solvent?

Personal Income and Expense Worksheet (Monthly)					
CASH IN		**CASH OUT**			
Alimony received		**2 TOTAL SAVINGS**		**Health Care Expenses**	
Child Support received		**Household Expenses**		Dental insurance	
Disability income		Electricity		Disability insurance	
Employer paid health insurance		Heat		Health insurance	
		Mortgage/CD payment		Life insurance	
Employer paid re-employment insurance		Property insurance		Medical insurance	
		Real estate taxes		Prescriptions	
Employer paid workers' compensation		Rent		Other medications	
		Repairs/maintenance		Other	
Food stamps		Telephone		**7 TOTAL HEALTH CARE**	
Fuel assistance income		Television cable		**Personal Expenses**	
Housing subsidy		Trash removal		Child, elder care	
Investment income		Water and sewer		Cleaning, laundry	
Medical assistance		Other		Clothing, shoes	
Net wages-self		Other		Dues, memberships	
Net wages-spouse		**3 TOTAL HOUSEHOLD**		Education, training	
Net wages-children		**Vehicle Expenses**		Entertainment	
Self-employment income		Gas, parking		Gifts, contributions	
Social security income		Repairs/maintenance		Hobbies, subscriptions	
TANF (public assistance)		Vehicle insurance		Travel, vacations	
Other		Vehicle loan payments		Other	
Other		Other		Other	
Other		Other		**8 TOTAL PERSONAL**	
Other		**4 TOTAL VEHICLE**		**Other Expenses**	
Other		**Food expenses**		Alimony paid	
Other		Dining out		Child care paid	
Other		Groceries		Credit card payments	
Other		Supplies		Income taxes	
Other		Other		Self-employment tax	
Other		Other		Student loan payments	
Other		Other		Other	
Other		Other		Other	
Other		**5 TOTAL FOOD**		Other	
Other		**School expenses**		**9 TOTAL OTHER**	
Other		Books		**10 TOTAL CASH OUT*** *add lines 2 through 9* OWNER DRAW?	
Other		Extracurricular			
Other		Tuition			
Other		Other		**11 CASH EXCESS (SHORTAGE)** *subtract line 10 from line 1*	
Other		Other			
1 TOTAL CASH IN		**6 TOTAL SCHOOL**			

WHAT DO YOU HAVE TO USE OR TO LOSE?

Assets are what we own. Liabilities are what we owe. The difference is our net worth. Remember Mike the Mechanic? He had boats and tools and a hunting shack. He had business equipment and a home. Mike ended up selling many of his assets to pay his bills. He ended up losing his home and everything he owned.

It's important for you to understand what your net worth is. Your net worth may be considered as collateral for a loan. If you have no net worth or a low net worth, you likely will not have sufficient collateral. What do you have that you are willing to put at risk? What are you willing to lose? If Mike had put thought into his net worth, he may have made different choices.

Worksheet—Personal Financial Statement

PERSONAL FINANCIAL STATEMENT—*PLEASE OMIT CENTS WHEN PREPARING THIS FORM*				
Note: If assets and liabilities are individually owned, circle "I" in the amount columns. If you and another person jointly own assets or liabilities, please circle "J" in the amount columns.				
ASSETS OWNED			**LIABILITIES OWED**	
Description	Estimated Market Value		Description	Outstanding Balance
Cash, checking (bank name, account #)	I	J	Mortgage on homestead	I J
Cash, savings (bank name, account #)	I	J	Mortgage on other real estate	I J
IRA or other retirement account (describe)	I	J	Installment loans accounts	I J
Auto #1 (make, model, year)	I	J	Revolving credit accounts	I J
Auto #2 (make, model, year)	I	J	Loans co-signed for others	I J
Life insurance: Cash value: $	I	J	Taxes owed	I J
Real estate (homestead address)	I	J	Other liabilities	I J
Real estate (other address)	I	J	Loans on insurance, retirement accounts or bank accounts	I J
Stocks, bonds, investments (describe)	I	J		
Personal assets (list on separate sheet)	I	J		
Other (list on separate sheet)	I	J		
TOTAL ASSETS			**TOTAL LIABILITIES**	
			PERSONAL NET WORTH (Total assets minus total liabilities)	

OTHER OBLIGATIONS THAT YOU OWE SUCH AS ALIMONY, CHILD SUPPORT OR SPOUSAL MAINTENANCE					
Description	**Amount**	**Past due?**	**Description**	**Amount**	**Past due?**
		No Yes			No Yes
		No Yes			No Yes
		No Yes			No Yes
		No Yes			No Yes
Are you a co-maker, endorser or guarantor on any loan or contract?	No Yes→		If yes, for whom and to whom?		Amount
Are there any unsatisfied judgments against you?	No Yes→		If yes, to whom owed?		Amount
Have you declared bankruptcy in the last ten years?	No Yes→		If yes, in what city and state?		Year

YOUR CREDIT REPORT

HOW TO GET YOUR CREDIT REPORT:

The Fair Credit Reporting Act requires that each of the three nationwide consumer reporting agencies – Equifax, Experian, and Trans Union – must provide you with a free copy of your credit report at least once every 12 months, at your request. This includes the information in your file and a list of everyone who has recently requested it.

Each of the three major reporting agencies keeps its own records that could differ slightly, so you will want to request a copy from each of them. The three agencies have set up one central website, toll-free phone number, and mailing address through which you can order your free annual credit report.

Visit the website at:
www.annualcreditreport.com

Call toll-free:
1-877-322-8228

Mail Request Form to:
**Annual Credit Report Request Service
PO Box 105281
Atlanta, GA 30348-5281**

You are also entitled to a free copy of your credit report if someone has taken adverse action against you, such as denying your application for credit or denying you employment. In this instance, you must make a request for your report within 60 days of receiving notice of the action. You are also entitled to one free report every 12 months if you are unemployed looking for work, are on welfare, or if your report is inaccurate due to fraud. To find out how to get your credit report from each agency, call or visit the following web addresses:

Experian   866-200-6020
www.experian.com/reportaccess/

Trans Union   800-888-4213
www.transunion.com

Equifax   800-685-1111
www.equifax.com

There are many other "free" credit reports that are widely advertised, but they are rarely what they seem. They may put you on telemarketing lists or have other hidden costs. We recommend using only the contact information provided here when requesting a copy of your credit report.

You and your spouse should request separate credit reports to check each person's credit rating.

Some communities have Credit Bureaus that may also obtain your credit report for you. Check the yellow pages of your telephone book.

The Federal Trade Commission provides consumer information about credit and publishes a number of free brochures available in print or downloadable format. Topics include: Identity Theft, Credit Repair, Fair Credit Reporting, Credit and Divorce, Getting Business Credit, Cosigning a Loan, and How to Dispute Credit Report Errors.

Contact the Federal Trade Commission at 202-326-2222, visit their website at **www.ftc.gov**, or write to: Public Reference Federal Trade Commission, CRC-240, Washington, DC 20580.

**Public Reference
Federal Trade Commission
Washington, DC 20580
(202) 326-2222
www.ftc.gov**

HOW WILL YOUR LIFE CHANGE?

For existing business owners, you already know that your life is much different now than it was before you had your business. Is it what you expected it to be? Are you spending your time the way you want to spend it?

For prospective business owners, you have a vision of yourself serenely doing whatever it is you choose to do in your business.

For both existing and prospective business owners, the question is, are you working *in* your business or *on* your business?

Working *in your business* means that you are *doing the tasks* required to keep the business operating successfully. It is likely, for existing business owners, you are so busy every day you barely have a chance to keep up with all of the work to be done.

Working *on your business* means that you are *overseeing and managing the work to be done*. Even if you are still doing all of the work, you have a clear understanding of each function you are performing; you are organized and able to keep up with what needs to be done.

In the Operations Planning section of this course you will be provided with tools to help you more clearly understand how to work *on* your business instead of *in* it.

Meanwhile, begin to think about your role in the business. What do you want it to be? What are you doing? What are you not doing?

For your personal life, what must you do in order to feel fulfilled, relaxed and happy? What commitments must you keep to your family, friends, hobbies and home?

You are already using up all of your time. When you own a business, or even in the business planning stages, you will be using your time in different ways. What time is available for change, and what time is not?

As you learn more about business planning and operating your business, you will begin to understand more about the types of choices you can make. In the meantime, track how you spend your time – take a personal inventory of what time you feel is valuable and what time you are willing or needing to alter.

WHAT DO YOU WANT TO DO? WHAT DON'T YOU WANT TO DO?

List your ideas below. You can revisit them at the end of this course.

_____

_____

_____

_____

_____

_____

_____

_____

_____

_____

_____

_____

_____

_____

_____

_____

_____

_____

CONTINGENCY PLANNING

"WHEN" INSTEAD OF "IF"

When something goes wrong, not *if* something goes wrong, what will you do? How often have you had to readjust your plan, change your mind, or try something else?

In business, something *will* always go wrong. In our personal lives, something *will* always go wrong. We never know what or when, but we know it will.

Contingency planning *prepares us* to adjust, rethink, or change course in strategic ways. It helps us "keep our balance," and "stay in step." It eases distress and prevents us from being devastated or overcome with stress or loss.

Personal finances – What if you incur a large loss, such as a major appliance, your car, or your house? How will you plan to adjust your personal finances? What if this business does not produce the amount of cash for you that you thought it would?

Lifestyle – What if you become injured or disabled? How will you keep your business operating?

Business issues – What if the marketplace changes and your sales drop? What if costs increase? What will you do to keep your business stable or growing?

Contingency planning is *being prepared for change,* with strategies that you have thought through *before* circumstances change.

Nearly everyone has lost a job or has suffered through periods of financial distress. All businesses have endured market changes. It's not what happens to us that tests our character and commitment, it's how we respond.

As you go through your business planning process, be aware of the risks and potential threats to both your business and your personal life. Be flexible and open-minded. Set goals. Measure your achievements. Know what you have to gain and to lose.

Stay in tune with trends and events that are impacting your business opportunities and your personal lifestyle. Be prepared to alter, adjust, change, redirect, reconstruct, or just plain stop doing what you are doing.

BUSINESS PLANNING

WHAT IS BUSINESS PLANNING?

Business planning is the process of designing and planning to build a business. It includes the elements discussed in this chapter.

WHAT IS A BUSINESS PLAN?

A business plan is a written document that describes a business opportunity.

WHAT DOES A BUSINESS PLAN CONTAIN?

In addition to an overview, which contains a **description of the business** – who owns it, where it is located, its legal structure, its history, what it sells, and what its mission is – a business plan should describe, in detail, three primary facets of the business:

Marketing Plan: Describes how the business will interact with the marketplace. Includes profiles of the customers, a description of the industry, the features and benefits of the products or services the business will sell, how the products or services will be distributed, the competition, the competitive advantages of the business, the position the business will have in the marketplace, and how the products and services will be promoted.

Operations Plan: Describes how the business will work. Includes descriptions of how the products and services will be produced, the types of goods and services the business will consume, the types of employees the business will employ, who will manage the business, licensing and zoning requirements, and other details about the business operations.

Financial (Cash Flow) Plan: Describes how the business will access and manage its financial resources, and what the profit and growth potential might be. Includes projected financial statements, primarily projected cash flow statements that depict sources and uses of cash. Specifically, a projected cash flow depicts the projected types and amounts of cash, and when the cash will be spent or received. It also includes footnotes that describe what assumptions were used to create the financial plan. If the business is an existing business, it also includes historical financial statements.

Do I Need to Include Additional Information?

You may also include attachments such as brochures describing the product or service, detailed descriptions of equipment to be purchased, price quotations from potential vendors, letters of intent from potential customers, résumés of the business owners and key partners or employees, collateral documents, and other data that supports the marketing, operations and financial plans. The number of attachments depends on the type of business.

WHY WRITE A BUSINESS PLAN?

To take risks on paper. By designing the business on paper, the owner and other resources (lenders, partners and vendors) can better assess the resources the business will need and the potential risks or rewards that may result. You can also begin to envision yourself owning and operating the business. This process of planning helps you understand not only the potential risks and rewards, but also the reality and desirability of what your day-to-day life will be like.

A written business plan reflects your ability to plan and organize your business concept and your depth of business knowledge. Potential lenders and investors will require a business plan. They will review the plan to assess risk. They evaluate your capability and character, and the potential feasibility and viability of the business.

You may be thinking, "Why should I spend my time writing a business plan? What's in it for me?"

Success is what's in it for you! Most (80%) of businesses fail within the first two years of their operation, usually due to poor planning and management. The creators of this course, the Northeast Entrepreneur Fund, Inc., have successfully achieved an *80% business survival rate*, the total *opposite* of the national business failure rate, by teaching this course to entrepreneurs like you. You can have a 20% chance of success without a plan, or you can have an 80% chance of success with a plan. What choice will you make?

DUE DILIGENCE

A business plan describes a variety of assumptions about the *future*. How can we tell what the future will bring?

A process called due diligence is used by lenders and business analysts. Using this process, the lender or analyst attempts to *verify and validate the assumptions of the business plan.* Throughout the business planning process, as information is researched and analyzed, the planner is practicing due diligence.

The due diligence process demands that we be objective and realistic. It is a tool for the entrepreneur to use to determine the reality of the assumptions the entrepreneur will make. If we say sales will be $50,000 in the first year, how can we verify or validate that this is an achievable goal? What information can we obtain that supports this claim?

The outcomes of due diligence are *verification and validation* of the following business characteristics:

Feasibility *Capable of being done, practicable, possible, likely, reasonable, probable, suitable.*	• There is a market for the product or service. • The plan presents a structure adequate for entering and serving the market. • The resources (money, marketing and management) exist or are accessible for entering and serving the market.
Viability *The stage of development that will permit the business to live and/or grow.*	• The plan presents opportunities for an ongoing relationship with the market, or the plan presents a specific relationship with the market that depicts a profitable interaction with the market.
Desirability *Worth wanting, pleasing, producing desired financial results.*	• The plan presents that the business should produce the income you are seeking. • Preparing the plan helped you see the reality of the work environment you will be involved in. You are prepared for and comfortable with the business environment, responsibilities and duties that the business will need you for.

HOW OTHER PEOPLE LOOK AT YOUR BUSINESS PLAN

All lenders and investors use a due diligence process to evaluate a prospective investment opportunity. The chart on the following page presents a sample business readiness assessment that is representative of the types of concerns and questions others will have about your business. This is an excellent guide for you to use when developing your plan – if you can't answer these questions when you are asked, the investment or loan you are seeking may not be forthcoming.

Sample Business Readiness Assessment Checklist

MARKET	
Products/Services	Is your product or service clearly identified?
Distribution	Have you identified appropriate methods of distribution for your product or service?
Industry	What knowledge do you have of the industry? What are the industry trends on a local, regional, and national and international basis?
Competition	Who will you be competing against? What are their strengths and weaknesses? How will your business compare?
Customer	What are the characteristics of your target customers? Who will you be selling your product or service to?
Position	What will be your position in the marketplace? Is it clearly identified? Will it be difficult to establish?
Packaging	How will you package your product or service? Is it appropriate? Do you have an appropriate location for your business?
Promotion	Do you have a plan to promote your product or service? Is it affordable?
Pricing	How will you determine pricing for your product or service? Will you price higher, lower, or the same as your competitors?
Selling	Who will be responsible for sales? What are their qualifications for selling your product or service?
MANAGEMENT	
Who will manage?	Will you manage the business yourself? If someone else will be managing your business, do they have the training, skills, and experience necessary?
Readiness	Have you researched and obtained the necessary licenses, permits, tax ID's, etc.?
Record keeping	Do you have a record keeping system in place?
Policies/procedures	Have you created policies and procedures for your business? Who will handle accounts, customer service, inventory management, etc.?
Risk management	Do you have the proper insurance in place?
MONEY	
Personal finances	Do you know your personal income, expenses and net worth?
Credit worthiness	Do you know your credit history? Have you obtained a copy of your credit report?
Cash flows	Have you done two years of cash flow projections for your business? Will the business be feasible in $ volume, owner draw, taxes, and sales projections?
Start up, working capital needs	Have you identified what you will need to get your business started? Do you have sufficient capital?
Breakeven	At what point will your business break even? Is it an attainable level? Can you continue to sell above that level? Do you want to?
Collateral	Do you have sufficient collateral for any loans you have or may need?
CONTINGENCIES	
Sales below projections	What will happen if you don't make your sales projections? How long can you maintain?
Expenses increase	What will happen if your expenses increase unexpectedly? Temporarily? Permanently?
Competitor aggression	How will you handle a competitor aiming to put you out of business? Can you survive?
Illness, emergency	Who will operate the business if you can't? Short term? Long term?
Can't make payments	How will you pay the bills of the business if the business can't?

CORE FOUR® Business Planning Course

BUSINESS PLAN OUTLINE

Use the following outline to *summarize* your business planning *decisions.* Title each section of your written plan as indicated in the outline. Write, in your own words, answers to the questions listed. Each question can be the start of a new paragraph. If a question does not apply, explain why it does not apply.

Tip: You don't have to win a Pulitzer Prize here. You don't have to be a great writer. The readers will care more about what the plan says than how it is written. Write the most clear and simple answers you can to the questions listed.

A) BUSINESS PLAN SUMMARY

1) Describe your products and services.

2) Describe the history of your business if it is an existing business, or how you developed your idea to start a new business.

3) Describe the legal structure of your business – sole proprietorship, partnership or corporation.

4) Describe your experience in this business and how it will help you succeed.

5) Describe your reason for believing the business will succeed.

B) MARKET PLANNING

1) <u>Products or Services</u>

   i) What customer need or want is being filled?

   ii) What are the features and benefits of your products or services?

   iii) How will your product be made or how will your services be provided?

   iv) Who will supply the materials?

   v) What future products/services will you offer, and when?

2) <u>Distribution</u>

   i) How will your products or services be distributed?

3) <u>Industry</u>

   i) What is happening in your industry (is it growing, stable or declining)?

   ii) What do you believe the future holds for this industry?

4) <u>Customers</u>

   i) Who are your customers – what does your customer profile look like?

   ii) How many customers will your business have?

   iii) What information do you have that supports your decisions about your customers?

   iv) What is the growth potential for this business? What is your plan for growth?

   v) What information do you have that supports your decisions about growth?

5) Competition

    i)   Who are your main competitors?

    ii)   What are their strengths and weaknesses?

6) Position

    i)   What will your market position be?

    ii)   What is your competitive advantage – why will customers buy from you instead of the competition?

7) Image and Packaging

    i)   What will the image of your business be?

    ii)   What will your packaging look like (attach samples)?

    iii) What do your business cards and promotional material look like (attach samples)?

    iv) Where will your business be located, and why did you choose this location? Include a sketch of your floor plan.

8) Pricing

    i)   How did you determine your pricing strategy?

    ii)   How do your prices compare to the competition?

9) Marketing Goals

    i)   What is your dream – where do you see your business in the next 2 to 5 years?
Example goals:
I want to start a successful business.
I want to expand my existing market share.
I want to add new products/services.

    ii)   What are your objectives for each of your goals? Why do you think they are realistic, how will they be measured, and when will they be achieved?
Example objectives:
I want to have a 10% profit margin in 12 months.
I will increase sales by 50% in 24 months.
I want to develop one new product/service within 18 months.

10) Marketing Strategy

    i)   What is your promotional plan?

C) OPERATIONS PLANNING

1) Who will handle which functions in the business?

2) What will their duties and qualifications be?

3) If employees, how many will you have and what will their duties be?

4) Who will hire, train and supervise them?

5) What will it cost your business for the first two years?

6) What will your owner draw be for the first two years?

7) What will your employee salaries be for the first two years?

8) Who will your lawyer, accountant, insurance agent, and other advisory team members be?

9) How will you manage your record keeping, finances, and inventory?

10) What licenses, permits or regulations will affect your business? (Attach copies of licenses, permits, or regulatory forms.)

11) Will you have to collect and pay sales tax, and if so, how much and for which entity (state or city)?

12) What types of insurance will you need (attach bids or copies of policy summary page)?

13) What types of payments will you accept (cash, check, credit cards, house accounts, etc.)?

14) What contingency plans have you made for *you*?

    i) What will you do if you become sick or are injured, or in the event of a family or personal emergency that takes you away from the business? Who will take care of the business? How much will it cost?

    ii) What will you do if your car breaks down?

    iii) What will you do if your day-care provider can't take care of your kid/s today, or if your kid/s are too sick to go to school?

15) What contingency plans have you made for the *business*?

    i) What will you do if sales are not what you expected? What will you do to increase them?

    ii) What will you do if costs are higher than you expected? What will you do to decrease them?

    iii) How will you make decisions to continue to stabilize or increase your cash flow and profits?

    iv) What will you do if a competitor lowers its prices?

D) CASH FLOW PLANNING

1) Include a month-by-month cash flow projection for at least the first two full years. Include written assumptions (explanations) supporting your projections.

If your business starts or the plan starts during a year, the first year projection will be a partial year. There should be two full years of projections after the partial year.

2) Include at least two years of financial statements for existing businesses. (If not in business two years, include what is available). Include, if possible, balance sheets and profit and loss statements.

3) Include your personal financial data: Personal Financial Statement (Assets, Liabilities and Net Worth) and a monthly income and expense statement (your personal financial plan).

E) ATTACHMENTS

Attachments should be provided to substantiate your claims in your plan. Always keep copies of the original documents for your files.)

1) Two years of personal income tax returns if requesting a loan.

2) Two years of business income tax returns.

3) Credit application (form from the lender) if requesting a loan.

4) Collateral documents (titles, abstracts, or other proofs of ownership) if requesting a loan.

5) Lists of assets to be acquired and their costs.

6) Resumés of yourself and others who will work in the business.

7) Market studies.

8) Articles from magazines, newspapers, or the World Wide Web.

9) Photographs, sketches of your products or floor plan, brochures describing your services.

10) Copies of leases or other contracts.

11) Letters of intent from customers to do business with you.

12) Examples of your brochures, business cards, stationery and other materials.

BRILLIANT CLEANING SERVICE

SALLY SPARKLE, PROPRIETOR

September 30, 20XX

BUSINESS PLAN SUMMARY

Brilliant Cleaning Service is a start-up business that provides cleaning services for residential homes. Primary services include floor, window, and bathroom care. The business is seeking $1,900 for equipment, supplies, and advertising.

The name and address of the business is:

Brilliant Cleaning Service
1111 Home Street
Hometown, USA 99999
Phone   123-456-7890
FAX   098-765-4321
Email   clean@yahoo.net

The name and address of the business owner is:
Sally Sparkle
1111 Home Street
Hometown, USA 99999

Market

The potential market for Brilliant Cleaning Service is 39% of households in the Hometown area. The average target customer is 35 to 65 years of age and earns $35,000 or more annually. There are three competitors serving the area. Brilliant's competitive advantage is that it can attract customers with a more personalized, professional cleaning that is "Satisfaction Guaranteed."

Organization Plan

This business is a sole proprietorship with no employees. The owner will manage the finances and perform the work.

BUSINESS DESCRIPTION

Nature of the Business

Brilliant Cleaning Service is an insured, residential cleaning service. It offers cleaning service tailored to its customers' needs. Most customers will likely request weekly cleaning. There is also a need to offer in-depth cleaning on an as-needed basis.

History of the Business
None - this is a start-up business.

Legal Structure of the Business
Sole proprietorship, Sally Sparkle, proprietor.

Past Work Experience
The owner has five years of experience as an employee for Merry Maids, Inc.

Reasons the Business Will Succeed
The belief that the business will succeed is based on the proprietor's knowledge, experience, and determination to succeed.

Services

Services provided include cleaning of floors, windows, cabinets, dishes, laundry, and furniture, and watering of houseplants.

This service will save the customer time and energy of doing the work. The customer has the benefit of enjoying a clean and attractive home. The customer also has extra leisure time for entertaining guests, enjoying hobbies, or any other activities.

Start-up money will be used for a vacuum cleaner, cleaning supplies, hand-held vacuum, buckets, rags and other miscellaneous supplies. See attached list and bids for equipment.

Brilliant Cleaning Service will provide cleaning supplies used. Ten homes cleaned weekly per month will cost approximately $40 per month (total) for cleaning supplies, which will be purchased from mass merchandisers such as Wal-Mart in Hometown. Driving to and from these homes will cost approximately $30 per month. Cleaning ten homes will take approximately 40 hours per week with an average cleaning time of four hours.

In the next two years, Brilliant Cleaning Service will expand its services to commercial customers and will hire employees to meet the new demand.

Distribution

Services will be directly supplied to the end-users in their homes.

Industry

There are many new, larger homes being built in the area. According to the city's building permits issued each year:

18 homes of over 3000 square feet were built one year ago.

21 homes of over 3000 square feet were built two years ago.

According to "Domestic Details" in *Income Opportunities* magazine, March 2XXX, more women were hiring cleaning services to ease the strain of their hectic lifestyles – over 20% of households surveyed had hired a cleaning service, an increase of 5% from the previous year.

Customers

The targeted customer profile includes working families. The ages range from 35 to 65 years. The average annual income is $35,000 or more. According to census information (see attached), from the population of 5,000 households, 21% of the households earned $35,000 or more. This means there are 1,050 customers who fit Brilliant's target profile. If 20% of these households use a cleaning service, that means 210 households could be potential customers. Brilliant's goal is to secure ten customers. It already has three potential customers – see attached letters of intent. An average customer would use Brilliant Cleaning Service once a week for an average cleaning time of four hours.

Competition

Brilliant Cleaning Service's main competitors are franchised cleaning services.

Service Cleaners, 1212 Clean Street, Hometown, USA. Strengths include name recognition and size. It has 20 employees and the largest number of customers. It is insured and the employees are bonded. Weakness is lack of consistency. A customer could have one employee clean their home one week, and have a different employee another week. It charges $60 for a half-day of cleaning.

Maids for Hire, 4000 Washboard Street, Hometown, USA. Strengths include name recognition and size. It has five employees and is the second largest provider of cleaning services. It is insured, but employees are not bonded. Weakness is also lack of consistency. It charges $55 for a half-day of cleaning.

Julie's, 3256 Duster Street, Hometown, USA. Strengths include individualized service since the owner, Julie, operates this business. Julie's weakness is she has no employees and is not insured. Julie has a regular customer base and has no room for new customers. She charges $35 for a half-day of cleaning.

Position in the Marketplace

Brilliant's position in the marketplace is mid-base residential. Brilliant's strengths include personal and professional service. Although the franchisers have strong advertising techniques, a sole proprietor has the advantage of offering more personalized service. This service gives Brilliant a competitive advantage because most customers prefer the same cleaning person for each cleaning.

Brilliant's competitive advantage over Julie's is its professionalism. Brilliant is insured and the owner and employees will wear uniforms for a professional image. Because of the owner's vast knowledge of houseplants, Brilliant will offer to take care of houseplants as an additional service no one else offers.

Image/Packaging

See attached bids for all promotional costs.

The business name is Brilliant Cleaning Service.

The slogan is: Professional Service By People Who Care!

The business will be operated out of the owner's home.

Business cards and flyers will cost approximately $200.

Magnetic car signs will cost approximately $160.

Printed bid forms and invoices will cost $40.

Uniforms include black pants and white shirt with business name. Uniforms will be provided by U.S. Linen Services for $40 per month, which includes the cleaning of the uniform.

Pricing

Brilliant will charge $45 for a half-day of cleaning. All prices will be quoted per job: by the size, time, and effort involved in cleaning the residence, not by an hourly rate. Brilliant's fees reflect a fair market rate, and are comparable to fees charged by competitors.

Marketing Goals and Objectives

To start the business by November (20XX).

To acquire ten customers by April (20YY).

To earn $1,200 monthly by June (20YY).

Marketing Strategy

Brilliant Cleaning Service will follow the promotion plan below to meet its goals and objectives:

Action	Responsibility	When	Cost
Order business cards/flyers	Owner	10/XX (Year)	$200
Magnetic vehicle signs	Owner	10/XX	$160
Invoices/Bids	Owner	10/XX	$40
Uniforms	Owner	10/XX	$40/month
Press release	Owner	10/XX	$0
Publish assumed name	Owner	10/XX	$25
Put up 25 flyers (check every two weeks)	Owner	10/XX	$0
Put ad in church newsletter (runs every other week)	Owner	11/XX	$5/week
Put ad in local paper in business directory (runs every Sunday)	Owner	11/XX	$50/month
Put ad in local paper in business directory	Owner	12/XX	$50/month
Yellow pages (starts in June)	Owner	3/XX	$15/month
Put ad in local paper in business directory	Owner	4/XX	$50/month
Put ad in local paper in business directory	Owner	5/XX	$50/month

After this – the owner will rely on word-of-mouth advertising.

OPERATING PLAN

Duties and Qualifications
The sole proprietor will perform all duties including cleaning, bidding, advertising and record keeping. The sole proprietor has five years experience in cleaning and has had one course on record keeping. The sole proprietor will take a monthly draw of $1,200.

Employees
There will be no employees in the first two years.

Specialists or Consultants
The sole proprietor will continue to consult monthly with a business consultant to set up record keeping systems and receive help with monitoring the business. The sole proprietor will use the services of Jones Accounting Services for income tax preparation.

Record Keeping, Inventory and Finances
The sole proprietor will use a manual record keeping system that is a combined cash receipts and cash disbursements journal.

The sole proprietor will use ledger sheets to track inventory supplies.

The sole proprietor will open a business checking account at National Bank, located in Hometown.

Licenses, Permits and Other Regulations
No licenses or permits are required to operate this business.

Brilliant is not required to get a hazardous waste permit. See attached letter from the State.

Sales Tax
Brilliant will have to collect 6.5% state sales tax from customers (to be paid to the state) on all services.

Brilliant does not have to collect a city sales tax.

Insurance
Brilliant Cleaning Service will get the following types of insurance from All-Types of Insurance, located in Hometown, USA – see attached bids:

Commercial Auto Insurance: $600 annual premium or $200 down and monthly payments of $35

General Liability: $300 annual premium

Worker's Compensation on owner: $350 annual premium

Payment Terms
Customer payments will be accepted by cash or check, which are collected at the end of each job. Payment terms will be explained to potential customers before accepting each job. If a customer does not pay at the end of a job, future work will not be done until payment is received. After six months of being in business, Brilliant will start accepting credit cards.

Hours Open
Brilliant Cleaning Service will operate Monday through Saturday, from 9:00 a.m. to 6:00 p.m.

Contingency Plans
There will be one day set aside biweekly-weekly for a make-up day in case of owner illness or emergency. If the owner gets sick, she will reschedule the appointment. If the job cannot wait, the owner will clean those despite illness or will get her sister to fill in on the job. If the owner gets injured on the job, Worker's Compensation will be available. If the owner is injured, her sister will fill in until the owner can get back to work.

If the owner's car breaks down, she can borrow her mother's car or take a taxi.

If sales are not as anticipated and loan payments cannot be made, owner will get part-time job in the evening. The owner will also look at increasing promotional efforts and reducing expenses, such as uniforms.

FINANCIAL PLAN

See two-year, monthly Cash-Flow Projections with List of Assumptions.

There are no Business Financial Statements since this is a start-up business.

See Personal Financial Statement.
See Personal Income and Expense worksheet.

ATTACHMENTS

1. Credit application
2. Years 20XX and 20YY personal income tax returns
3. Copies of collateral documents
4. Resumé
5. Census data
6. Article from *Income Opportunities* magazine
7. Letters of intent from: B. Barney, M. Wilson, S. Jacobson
8. Bids for business cards, flyers, magnetic car signs, and uniforms
9. Sample business cars, flyers and magnetic car signs
10. Sample invoices and bid sheets
11. Quotes for ads in local newspaper
12. Insurance quotes

START-UP EXPENSES

Expense	Cost
Vacuums	200
Supplies and Misc.	110
Business cards/flyers	200
Signs	160
Uniforms	40
Cleaning supplies	40
Insurance	850
Assumed name filing	25
Phone deposit	50
Working capital	825
TOTAL	$2,500
Sources	
Owner Contribution	600
Loan	1,900
TOTAL	$2,500

BRILLIANT CLEANING SERVICE, SALLY SPARKLE, PROPRIETOR
CASH FLOW PROJECTIONS FOR YEAR ENDED DECEMBER 31, 20XX
(*) = startup month

		Jan	Feb	Mar	Apr	May	Jun	Jul	Aug	Sep	Oct(*)	Nov	Dec	Totals
1	**Sales**													
2	Seasonal homes											180	450	630
3	Repeat homes											900	1080	1,980
4	**Cash IN from sales**											1,080	1,530	2,610
5	**Goods**													
6	Cleaning supplies										40	20	35	95
7	**Cash OUT for goods**										40	20	35	95
8	**Operations**													
9	Health/WC										350			350
10	Acctg, legal										8	8	8	24
11	Advert/promo										360	60	60	480
12	Bank, cr card chgs										45	12	12	69
13	Auto expenses											20	55	75
14	Insurance, gen liab										500	35	35	570
15	Misc - uniforms										40	40	40	120
16	Office supplies										110		25	135
17	Repairs/maint											5	5	10
18	Taxes & licenses										25			25
19	Telephone										50	20	20	90
20	**Cash OUT operations**										1,488	200	260	1,948
21	Other cash in													
22	Loan proceeds										1,900			1,900
23	Owner contrib										600			600
24	Sales tax collected											70	99	169
25	**Total other cash IN**										2,500	70	99	2,669
26	Other cash out													
27	Sales tax paid													
28	Debt service													
29	Capital equipment										200			200
30	Bldgs/improvements													
31	Owner draw													
32	**Total other cash OUT**										200			200
33	**Net change in cash**										772	(220)	69	621
34	**Beginning cash**										0	772	552	0
35	**Ending cash**										772	552	621	621

BRILLIANT CLEANING SERVICE, SALLY SPARKLE, PROPRIETOR
CASH FLOW PROJECTIONS FOR YEAR ENDED DECEMBER 31, 20YY

		Jan	Feb	Mar	Apr	May	Jun	Jul	Aug	Sep	Oct	Nov	Dec	Totals
1	**Sales**													
2	Seasonal homes				270	270						180	270	990
3	Repeat homes	1,440	1,440	1,440	1,800	1,800	1,800	1,800	1,800	1,800	1,800	1,800	1,800	20,520
4	**Cash IN from sales**	1,440	1,440	1,440	2,070	2,070	1,800	1,800	1,800	1,800	1,800	1,980	2,070	21,510
5	**Goods**													
6	Cleaning supplies	35	35	35	40	40	40	40	40	40	40	45	45	475
7	**Cash OUT for goods**	35	35	35	40	40	40	40	40	40	40	45	45	475
8	**Operations**													
9	Health/WC											350		350
10	Acctg, legal	8	8	83	8	8	8	8	8	8	8	8	8	171
11	Advert/promo	10	10	10	60	60	25	15	15	15	15	15	15	265
12	Bank, cr card chgs	12	12	12	12	12	12	12	12	12	12	12	12	144
13	Auto expenses	25	30	55	30	30	55	230	30	55	30	30	55	655
14	Insurance, gen liab	35	35	35	35	35	35	35	35	35	35	850	35	1,235
15	Misc - uniforms	40	40	40	40	40	40	40	40	40	40	40	65	505
16	Office supplies						50						50	100
17	Repairs/maint	5	5	5	5	5	5	5	5	5	5	5	5	60
18	Taxes & licenses													
19	Telephone	20	20	20	20	20	20	20	20	20	20	20	20	240
20	**Cash OUT operations**	155	160	260	210	210	250	365	165	190	165	1,330	265	3,725
21	**Other cash in**													
22	Loan proceeds													
23	Owner contrib													
24	Sales tax collected	94	94	94	135	135	117	117	117	117	117	129	135	1,401
25	**Total other cash IN**	94	94	94	135	135	117	117	117	117	117	129	135	1,401
26	**Other cash out**													
27	Sales tax paid	169			282			387			351			1,189
28	Debt service	65	65	65	65	65	65	65	65	65	65	65	65	780
29	Capital equipment													
30	Bldgs/improvements													
31	Owner draw	1,380	1,380	1,380	1,380	1,380	1,380	1,380	1,380	1,380	1,380	1,380	1,380	16,560
32	**Total other cash OUT**	1,614	1,445	1,445	1,727	1,445	1,445	1,832	1,445	1,445	1,796	1,445	1,445	18,529
33	Net change in cash	(270)	(106)	(206)	228	510	182	(320)	267	242	(84)	(711)	450	182
34	Beginning cash	621	351	245	39	267	777	959	639	906	1,148	1,064	353	621
35	Ending cash	351	245	39	267	777	959	639	906	1,148	1,064	353	803	803

ASSUMPTIONS FOR CASH FLOW PROJECTION

Note: Assumption number corresponds to line number on cash flow projections. Items without an assumption number are not applicable and therefore not included on the cash flow projections; however, explanations of these items are included below.

1) Sales

2) Seasonal Customers: Average $45 per half-day of cleaning. The business will have customers who want their homes cleaned for the holidays.

November - four customers
December - ten customers
April - six customers
May - six customers
November - four customers
December - six customers
April - six customers
May - eight customers
November - six customers
December - eight customers

3) Repeat Customers: Average $45 per half-day of cleaning once a week.

November - five customers
by December - six customers
by January - eight customers
by April - ten customers

5) Cash Out for Goods

6) Cleanings supplies - for ten homes per month (cleaned weekly) will cost approximately $40 per month.

8) Cash Out for Operations

-) Gross Wages, Payroll Taxes - not applicable since the owner will not have any other employees.

9) Worker's Compensation Insurance - $350 annual premium to cover owner.

10) Accounting and Professional Services - $8 per month for consulting services and $75 in March 20XX and 20YY to have taxes done.

11) Advertising - see marketing strategy in business plan.

-) Bad Debts - based on past experience, bad debts are not incurred.

12) Bank - $45 to open account and get checks, monthly service fee of $12.

13) Auto - Driving to and from cleaning jobs will cost approximately $30 per month for ten homes cleaned weekly. In December, March, June, September and December the owner will spend $25 for oil change. In July, the owner will need to get new tires for approximately $200.

14) Insurance - Commercial auto insurance is $600 annually - $200 down payment and $35 per month. General Liability is $300 annually.

15) Miscellaneous - $40 per month for uniforms; a $25 contingency in December of each year.

16) Office Supplies - $110 for supplies and invoices, will need to replenish about every six months.

-) Rent - Not applicable.

17) Repairs and Maintenance - Will plan for $5 to cover costs for vacuum cleaner bags and belts.

18) Taxes and Licenses - $25 to file assumed name.

19) Telephone - $50 deposit and $20 monthly service charge.

22) Loan Proceeds - $1,900 at 13.25%, 36 months, closed in November, monthly payments of $65 start in December.

23) Owners Contribution - $600 from savings.

24/27) Sales Tax – The owner will collect 6.5% on services to be paid out quarterly.

31) Owners Draw – The owner will draw $1,000 per month to start with a goal of $1,200 per month by April, 20YY.

ATTACHMENTS

- Credit Application
- Credit History Report
- Two Years of Personal Tax Returns
- Two-Years Business Tax Returns (NA)
- Collateral Documents
- Resumes
- Market Studies
- Articles from Magazines
- Photographs/Sketches of Work
- Leases
- Contracts for Equipment, Outside Services, Cost of Goods, etc.
- Letter of Intent
- Bids for Brochures, Business Cards, Stationary, and Other Promotional Pieces, Signs
- Insurance Quotes
- Remodeling Quotes (20% added for contingencies)
- Articles of Incorporation
- Purchase Agreements
- Floor Plans
- Personal Income and Expense Worksheet
- Copies of Licenses and/or Permits

THE SCRAPBOOK NOOK

1500 James Street
Lakeville, MN 12345

Business Plan

Submitted by

Ann and David Smith
January 5, 20XX

Table of Contents

1.0   EXECUTIVE SUMMARY

Mission Statement
The Scrapbook Nook is committed to providing customers a variety of products and services dedicated to scrapbooking. We understand the hobby of scrapbooking and want to mentor those just learning the basics of this craft to ensure each one's continued success and interest. We will also provide more experienced scrapbookers the opportunity to purchase new and exciting products as they become available.

Overview
*   This business will be a partnership between Ann and David Smith.
*   There will not be any non-family employees at this time.
*   Location will be a leased building at 1500 James Street in Lakeville, MN.
*   Floor space will be approximately 800 s.f. with the option to expand to 1200 s.f. Area is divided into sales floor and workroom where customers can work on scrapbooks or take classes.
*   The space is located on ground level with large windows looking over James Street. There is a bathroom.
*   Parking space available in the rear for five cars and street parking in front of the store.
*   Stock will include paper, adhesives, cutting supplies, punches, stickers, albums, storage materials, reference books, pens, markers, die cuts, and embellishments.
*   Services will include classes on various scrapbook techniques and crops (a dedicated time for scrapbooking in a social atmosphere where customers can buy what they need from the store while they work in the facility workroom).
*   Investment will be from personal finances and business loan.
*   This is a new business with a vision of capturing the area market and expanding selection of stock and options for classes and scrapbooking events.

History of the Industry and Current Need
Scrapbooking is the art of putting together photos, memorabilia, and embellishments into a work of art. It entails not only making sure the photographs will be safely preserved for years to come, but also that the actual memory will be saved through journaling. Although the keeping of scrapbooks dates back to earlier centuries, the craft of scrapbooking is booming today.

The Craft Connection, a craft and hobby trade group, reported in 2000 that scrapbooking ranked among the top five hobbies in terms of participation in the United States. This industry was described as a $500 million business at that time.

"The Scrapbook Report", a study of the scrapbooking industry undertaken by Johnson & Dell has just released its findings that US consumers now spend $1.4 billion on scrapbooking supplies each year. The data also show that 21 percent of US households have participated in scrapbooking activities during the last year. It is also important to note that only 34% of those who scrapbooked considered themselves novices. This hobby is much more than a trend where one tries it out and quits soon after. Sixty-six percent in this study described themselves as intermediate or dedicated.

The typical scrapbooker has been identified by trade groups as mostly less than 40 years of age, higher income levels, and almost half are employed full time. This customer base has the financial means to support his or her scrapbooking hobby that requires ongoing investment.

With these facts in mind, The Scrapbook Nook will be entering into a market that is open in our geographical area. Local scrappers do not have a large selection of supplies. There is only one other specialty scrapbook store in a seventy-mile radius. That store is located approximately 30 miles from The Scrapbook Nook. Only Scrapbooks Plus and Cut 'N' Create, two home party suppliers, have classes or crops available and these choices are very limited in variety and accessibility. This area is in need of a store that offers a superior selection of high-quality scrapbook supplies and services.

2.0   ORGANIZATION

Co-owners' Individual Responsibilities
David Smith will be responsible for managing issues related to ordering supplies, inventory, and facility maintenance.

He will take on these duties, as he is very comfortable working with vendors, making telephone contact, and dealing with difficulties and complaints. His personality is very even and he has good communication skills. Last spring, David completed an Interpersonal Communications class and a Freshman Composition class at Lakeville Community College. Both of these courses provided information related to various communications and he received a "B" in each course.

David is very comfortable with most repair and maintenance duties. He recently built a large addition to his home that included laundry, bathroom, and living facilities. He has also remodeled a rental home that he manages.

David has worked with the Small Business Program at Lakeville Community College and plans to continue to do so as this business grows. He will also be attending the week-long training offered by Scrapbooks, Inc. in February for those interested in opening a scrapbook store.

That training will include:

Location and lease considerations	Tenant improvements
Product lines and distributors	Individual product profitability
Startup costs and considerations	Initial inventory/office equipment
Merchandising and displays	Furnishings
Signage and signs	Employees and hiring
Incentives	Point of sale software
Security	Marketing and free marketing
Competition and non-competes	Workshops and demonstrations
Retail scams	Purchasing and distributors
Forms and policies	Inventory control
Banking and merchant accounts	Children and liabilities
Returns and scams	

Ann Smith will be responsible for setting up and teaching classes, organizing and running crops, store displays, and newsletter production.

Ann is very comfortable with teaching. Her current position as a social studies instructor at Lakeville High School prepares her for designing and carrying out instruction. Her experience as a scrapper for over five years gives her the ability to plan and initiate classes that are meaningful. She has attended classes, crops, and conventions related to scrapbooking herself.

Ann has worked as an instructor with the Lakeville High School newspaper and yearbook staff, and would be able to design newsletters easily for this business.

Marketing will be a new area for Ann, and she will need to rely on the consultants from other scrapbook organizations and from the small business program at Lakeville Community College for external marketing information. Internal displays have already been in the process of design. Ann has many sample display pages that showcase various techniques and products.

Ann has taken small business classes at Lakeville Community College as well as bookkeeping and photography. She will be attending the February training as described above with David.

<u>**Co-owners' Combined Responsibilities**</u>
Both Ann and David will share in decision making while keeping the business mission in mind. They will also share hours worked in sales at the store. Each plans to keep his/her present employment and work in the business during off hours until the business shows a profit. Ann currently works 1080 hours/year and David works 2080 hours/year in outside employment. Ann has extended periods of time off during the year, and she is usually able to leave at 2:30 p.m. on days she works. David can vary shifts, mostly working days or afternoons.

The long-range goal is for David to quit his job when the business is successful enough to handle an owner's draw of $1500/month. Ann plans to remain at place of employment. Ann can carry all insurance for the family, a benefit that would be very expensive to replicate in a small business. Her salary is also much higher for the lower number of hours worked per year than David's and would be able to support the family more easily during rough times in the business.

<u>**Supplemental Help**</u>
Ann and David's son will be able to work the store to help out. He will be turning sixteen and has basic scrapbooking skills. He will need to train with his parents for a while since he has never held a retail position previously. He is a hard worker and very responsible.

Both Ann and David's parents live locally and have had retail experience. They will help if needed.

3.0 MANAGEMENT

Ann Smith
- Master's degree – Northern State University
- Business-related courses – Lakeville Community College
- Excellent communication skills
- Supervised health care needs of multiple clients
- Develops and implements various training to industry
- Develops classroom activities/manages classroom
- Scrapbook experience over five years
- Will complete comprehensive training for scrapbook store owners

David Smith
- Radio communication education– United States Army
- Served six years in United States Army
- Effective interpersonal skills
- Experience in construction trades
- Creates craft/wood items – enjoys arts

Consultants
- Scrapbooks, Inc. (Brian Jensen) Springfield, IL
- Provide extensive week-long training
- Have consulted over 200 scrapbooking stores nationwide
- Program is guaranteed to save 75% in startup inventory costs
- Program is endorsed by scrapbook industry's leading personalities and manufacturers
- Ongoing advice and training by phone for one year
- Subscription to industry marketing and idea newsletter for 6 months

4.0   MARKETING

Target Market
In the United States it is reported that last year, 21% of households had at least one person participate in scrapbooking. The typical "scrapper" is under age 40, employed, has a higher income and has children living at home.

Analysis of our surrounding area including Lakeville, Greendale, Oak Park, Cedar Valley, Brower, and Kelley shows a population of 28,611 according to the 2000 Census data. There are 12,391 total households accounted for, therefore, it can be inferred that 2602 households in our immediate area would purchase scrapbook supplies. Current scrapbook store owners have reported average customer sales of between $20 and $30 per visit. Almost half of scrapbook enthusiasts report spending more than $200 in a six-month period.

It has been further determined that more than 80% of scrapbookers shop for supplies in specialty stores. This fact increases the likelihood that our target market will seek out The Scrapbook Nook as his or her source of supplies in this region. We may also attract customers from the Janeville area.

Marketing will include an initial opening ad in the newspaper, Lakeville Daily Press business page story, radio spots announcing opening, and flyers. Flyers will be designed by Ann and copied onto colored paper. It is likely that our target market will utilize day care so we will provide flyers to local daycares and ask that they be distributed to parents. Flyers will be put up at community bulletin boards in Lakeville, Greendale, Oak Park, Cedar Valley, Brower, Kelley, and Janeville. Notices will be sent to all friends and family in the area via mail and/or e-mail asking that the word be spread. We will send flyers to churches to be given to women's groups, Girl Scout troops, and other various organizations. The scrapbook club in Greendale will receive flyers also.

Contact will also be made with all photo developing companies in the area and flyers and/or business cards will be provided. It is documented that people who scrapbook purchase much greater amounts of film than the national household average of six rolls per year.

Ann will plan a scrapbooking class to be offered through community education in the Lakeville, Greendale, and Brower areas for a small fee. This class, "Simple Scrapping" is fun and appropriate for both new and experienced scrappers.

Outside signage will include two storefront signs: one over the front window, the other on the north side of the building so that southbound traffic will face the sign directly. The front window will have two hanging grid wall displays that will be changed weekly by Ann once the store is opened. Prior to opening, the window will display a sign announcing the store coming soon.

On-going marketing will include monthly newsletters highlighting new products, tips for scrapbooking, class schedule, contest information, and coupons. These will be distributed to customers at the counter and mailed to our mailing list.

We will need to be very alert to cues given by store visitors of other avenues of marketing or groups of people that may be interested in scrapbook supplies. It will be important to keep our name heard. We will have a few shirts printed with our store name for family and friends to wear.

Our business cards will be simple, yet eye catching. Two opposite corners will have photo corners done in black. The card will be vertically printed. Store stationery will have the same design, except the photo corners will be in all four corners.

Concerns
The biggest drawback for any business in our area is the plight of local mining companies. It cannot be denied that cutbacks in the mining industry will lead to less money in the marketplace. The positive side to this problem is that people may spend more time at home and have additional time for scrapping. There will need to be consideration when deciding on product line where the most value lies.

Another drawback for this area will be the aging of the population. This hobby has a majority of followers under the age of 40 with children at home. Our business must encourage older customers to complete albums that can be handed down to their children or grandchildren. A special class will be developed for grandparents and will be marketed through the area senior citizens centers.

5.0   PRODUCT LINE AND SERVICES

Competition

Given that 80% of scrapbookers shop for supplies at a specialty store, our product line must not replicate the local competition. There are seven main competitors in this area. Appendix A shows a table comparing each.

The Lakeville Plaza and Anderson Drug are both large retail stores that purchase in very large quantities that enable them to have extremely low prices on some products. In Lakeville, Anderson Drug has pulled out of the scrapbooking market to a large extent. The Lakeville Plaza, on the other hand, dedicates about 10 feet of wall space to the hobby. The inventory is very basic and consists mostly of pre-packaged materials that give you little choice in what you are getting. Scrappers like to choose individual sheets of paper and stickers to work with specific pictures or layouts.

Carol's Crafts is a fabric and craft store with a variety of products. This business also dedicates a small area of store space to scrapbooking. They do carry some individual 8½x11 papers, but the choice is very limited and the pattern choices offered have become very stagnant. They are at a slight advantage over the large chain stores because they have clerks who usually are somewhat knowledgeable about crafts. The current manager of Carol's Crafts told me recently that she thought Lakeville could support a dedicated scrapbook store and they had conveyed that information to the mall management.

Internet stores are widely available, but there are not any classes or individual attention. You are not able to handle products before you see them and it is hard to match colors online. It is convenient to order from home, and the selection is very great.

Home party sales through Scrapbooks Plus (SP) and Cut 'N' Create (CNC) are available in the area. CNC is not widely represented in this area. There is one active consultant in the Bailey Lake area. There are several SP consultants, however. The current SP consultant in Greendale has a large following for her crops and classes. She has just put her house up for sale and is moving out of the area soon. An active consultant in the Bailey Lake area has been trying to recruit Ann for some time since she is unable to meet all of the requests she receives for classes and products. Scrapbooks Plus has high quality materials, but the selection is limited to their product line. There are no store hours and the parties are held in your home with you inviting the guests. This organization is great for introducing people to scrapbooking. Once the customers become more advanced or interested in the hobby it is likely they will look for more variety of product lines elsewhere.

The largest source of competition comes from The Memory Hut, a specialty scrapbooking store located in Bailey Lake. This business carries a large amount of paper and stickers and has other supplies necessary for scrappers. The owner is very helpful and has a well-organized web site to sell the product over also. He does a brisk business and talked about opening another store in Springdale. His store is an old building and the décor is very outdated. His cropping and class area is too small. The setting is a big drawback to his business.

Classes

The Scrapbook Nook will provide classes on a variety of topics for $10 each (including some basic supplies). There will be a class evaluation after each session to be used in future planning. The first month's topics will be determined based on feedback from the scrapbook teacher's web group Ann belongs to and will include:
* Simple Scrapping – simple ways to quickly put together a page using a variety of borders

- Beginning Scrapbooking – beginner class, introduction to tools and procedures
- Added Twists – use of wire to embellish
- Sleek Additions – adding vellum to your pages

Crops

The Scrapbook Nook will have crops every other Friday and one weekday per month. These crops will run from 6 p.m. until 12 midnight. The cost will be $10 and customers will be given a name tag that has been numbered. During the night, any product that is needed can be brought to the counter and listed under the customer's number. At the end of the night, the entire list will be rung up at one time. This makes it convenient for both the salesperson and the customer. There will be coffee, pop, and snacks available during the crop. One door prize drawing will be held and one contest with prize will be played during each crop. A small gift back with some paper/stickers will be given to each participant.

Retreats

The Scrapbook Nook would like to eventually have a weekend retreat planned at a nearby bed and breakfast or resort. This would require much planning and pricing but would begin to be researched after about 3-4 months of business.

Workroom Use

The Scrapbook Nook will have the workroom open during store hours when there is not a class or crop being held. There is currently seating for eight people. In the area, there will be punches, paper cutters, decorative scissors, and stencils that can be used if the paper is purchased from our store. A running tab can be kept at the front desk until the scrapper is ready to leave. There will not be a charge at this time for use of the machine. Long range plans include purchasing die cutting equipment and then a $2 per hour fee will be implemented.

Product

The Scrapbook Nook will be buying a start-up inventory kit from Scrapbooks, Inc. The cost of the kit is $35,000. This includes a full line of specialty papers from a variety of vendors, huge variety of stickers and sticker borders, organizational materials, paper cutters and scissors, page kits, adhesives albums, protective covers, large selection of pens, technique books, and die cuts. The kit saves money for the new store owner since many different company's products are highlighted in smaller quantities. This helps eliminate overstock on some products since manufacturers typically have high minimums on each order. The cost of the kit also includes one of the consultants flying out to the store for three days and helping set up and inventory all of the supplies in the point of sale system.

In talking with a recent purchaser of this kit, she told us the materials filled her 1200 s.f. store and gave her an excellent selection of many products in smaller amounts. She felt this helped her decide what sold in her area without being stuck with a large quantity of product that did not move. She also was extremely happy with the work accomplished quickly by the consultant who came to her store for set-up.

The Scrapbook Nook will fill a void in this region. The competitors that are close by do not offer classes that are convenient and varied. There is a limited choice of papers and stickers currently offered for consumers. None of the competitors showcase current trends such as ilets, beads, wire, or chucky embellishments. The Scrapbook Nook will offer such products and services for new and experienced scrapbookers.

Web Site

In the future, a web site that allows online purchasing will be added to the offerings. The site will include our newsletter sent to those who sign up. This will cut down on mailing costs since many people will be able to be reached through this service.

6.0 FINANCIALS

Costs required for the start-up of this business are listed in the appendix, page 10.

Two-year projections for The Scrapbook Nook's Cash Flow can be found in the appendix, pages 11-12.

Assumptions based on research used in determining the figures include the following:

1. 2602 households in this geographical area would purchase scrapbook supplies during the year.
2. $30 per customer sale is average according to scrapbook retailers.
3. Eighty percent of those scrapbooking households in our region would make one $30 purchase per year at The Scrapbook Nook during the first year.
4. Scrapbook supply sales will be reduced during the summer months when hobbyists take part in more outside activities.
5. November and December will be higher sales months because of holiday gift purchases.
6. Crop and class attendance will be reduced during the summer months.
7. Through expanded product line, classes, crops, and newsletters, sales will increase approximately 6% during year two.

Scrapbook Nook Startup Costs

Legal	75
Marketing	750
Business Insurance	250
POS Software	995
Rent Deposit	1200
Office/Store Supplies	175
Inventory	35000
Training	2476
Barcode Scanner	189
Receipt printer	319
Cash register	275
Computer	995
Printer	159
Shelving	7489
Signs	395
Total	**50742**

Funding

Owner contribution	12500
Lender/Bank	38242

#		START	Jan	Feb	Mar	Apr	May	Jun	Jul	Aug	Sept	Oct	Nov	Dec	TOTALS	% Sales
1	TOTAL SALES					6,000	6,880	4,920	4,720	5,070	5,745	7,105	7,730	7,685	55,855	100.0%
2	Merchandise sales					6,000	6,500	4,700	4,500	4,850	5,325	6,625	7,250	7,525	53,275	95.4%
3	Class tuition						200	100	100	100	240	240	240	100	1,320	2.4%
4	Crop fees						180	120	120	120	180	240	240	60	1,260	2.3%
5	TOTAL CASH IN FROM SALES					6,000	6,880	4,920	4,720	5,070	5,745	7,105	7,730	7,685	55,855	200.0%
6	CASH OUT FOR GOODS:															
7	Purchase for inventory	35,000				2,861	3,100	2,241	2,146	2,313	2,839	3,775	3,774	3,589	61,638	110.4%
8																
9	TOTAL CASH OUT FOR GOODS	(35,000)				(2,861)	(3,100)	(2,241)	(2,146)	(2,313)	(2,839)	(3,775)	(3,774)	(3,589)	(61,638)	-110.4%
10	CASH OUT FOR OPERATIONS															
11	Rent	600				600	600	600	600	600	600	600	600	600	6,000	10.7%
12	Ins-gen'l liab	250				60	60	60	60	60	60	60	60	60	790	1.4%
13	Telephone					80	80	80	80	80	80	80	80	80	720	1.3%
14	Advertising	750				80	80	80	100	100	100	135	135	135	1,695	3.0%
15	Office supplies	175				35	35	35	35	35	35	35	35	35	490	0.9%
16	Store supplies	995				50	50	50	50	50	50	90	90	90	1,565	2.8%
17	Postage					15	15	15	15	15	15	15	15	15	135	0.2%
18	Bank fees					5	5	5	5	5	5	5	5	5	45	0.1%
19	Legal & Accounting	75													75	0.1%
20	Training	2,476													2,476	4.4%
21																
22	TOTAL CASH OUT FOR OPERATIONS	(5,321)				(925)	(925)	(925)	(945)	(945)	(945)	(1,020)	(1,020)	(1,020)	(13,991)	-25.0%
23	NET CASH FROM OPERATIONS	(40,321)				2,214	2,855	1,754	1,629	1,812	1,961	2,310	2,936	3,076	(19,774)	-35.4%
24	OTHER CASH IN															
25	Loan proceeds - Microenterprise loan/Bank	38,242													38,242	68.5%
26	Owner contributions	12,500													12,500	22.4%
28	TOTAL OTHER CASH IN	50,742													50,742	90.8%
29	OTHER CASH OUT															
30	Closing costs															
31	P&I Debt Service					790	790	790	790	790	790	790	790	790	7,110	12.7%
32	Owner Draw								500	500	500	500	500	600	3,100	5.6%
33	Taxes, on Owner Draw															
34	Working capital	600													600	1.1%
35	Equipment	9,821				60	60	60	60	60	60	60	60	60	10,361	18.5%
36	TOTAL OTHER CASH OUT	(10,421)				(850)	(850)	(850)	(1,350)	(1,350)	(1,350)	(1,350)	(1,350)	(1,450)	(21,171)	-37.9%
37	NET CHANGE IN CASH					1,364	2,005	904	279	462	611	960	1,586	1,626	9,797	17.5%
38	BEGINNING CASH	1	1	1	1	1	1,365	3,370	4,273	4,552	5,014	5,625	6,585	8,171	1	0.0%
39	ENDING CASH BALANCE	1	1	1	1	1,365	3,370	4,273	4,552	5,014	5,625	6,585	8,171	9,798	9,798	17.5%

These projections present information that is the representation of the business owner/manager for the purpose of business planning, and should not be used for any other purpose. These projections do not include an evaluation of the assumptions or any form of assurance of the achievability of the projections.

Northeast Entrepreneur Fund, Inc.

CORE FOUR® Business Plan, Sample Business Plan, Scrapbook Nook Cash Flow Projections

SCRAPBOOK NOOK   CASH FLOW PROJECTION FOR YEAR ENDING – Second Calendar Year

	Jan	Feb	Mar	Apr	May	Jun	Jul	Aug	Sept	Oct	Nov	Dec	TOTALS	% Sales
1 TOTAL SALES	6,890	6,690	7,190	7,420	6,930	4,950	4,750	5,150	5,980	7,430	8,830	8,000	80,210	100.0%
2 Merchandise sales	6,450	6,250	6,750	7,000	6,510	4,710	4,510	4,910	5,500	6,950	8,350	7,790	75,680	94.4%
3 Class tuition	200	200	200	220	220	110	110	110	260	260	260	110	2,260	2.8%
4 Crop fees	240	240	240	200	200	130	130	130	220	220	220	100	2,270	2.8%
5 TOTAL CASH IN FROM SALES	6,890	6,690	7,190	7,420	6,930	4,950	4,750	5,150	5,980	7,430	8,830	8,000	80,210	200.0%
6 CASH OUT FOR GOODS:														
7 Purchase for inventory	3,044	2,950	3,745	3,864	3,073	2,223	2,129	2,318	3,596	3,280	3,941	3,677	37,840	47.2%
8														
9 TOTAL CASH OUT FOR GOODS	(3,044)	(2,950)	(3,745)	(3,864)	(3,073)	(2,223)	(2,129)	(2,318)	(3,596)	(3,280)	(3,941)	(3,677)	(37,840)	-47.2%
10 CASH OUT FOR OPERATIONS														
11 Rent	650	650	650	650	650	650	650	650	650	650	650	650	7,800	9.7%
12 Ins-gen'l liab	60	60	60	60	60	60	60	60	60	60	60	60	720	0.9%
13 Telephone	80	80	80	80	80	80	80	80	80	80	80	80	960	1.2%
14 Advertising	138	134	144	148	139	99	95	103	120	164	177	160	1,620	2.0%
15 Office supplies	35	35	35	35	35	35	35	35	35	35	35	35	420	0.5%
16 Store supplies	50	50	50	50	50	50	50	50	50	90	90	90	720	0.9%
17 Postage	15	15	15	15	15	15	15	15	15	15	15	15	180	0.2%
18 Bank fees	5	5	5	5	5	5	5	5	5	5	5	5	60	0.1%
19 Legal & Accounting														
20 Training														
21														
22 TOTAL CASH OUT FOR OPERATIONS	(1,033)	(1,029)	(1,039)	(1,043)	(1,034)	(994)	(990)	(998)	(1,015)	(1,099)	(1,112)	(1,095)	(12,480)	-15.6%
23 NET CASH FROM OPERATIONS	2,813	2,711	2,406	2,513	2,824	1,733	1,631	1,834	1,369	3,051	3,777	3,228	29,890	37.3%
24 OTHER CASH IN														
25 Loan proceeds - Microenterprise loan/Bank														
26 Owner contributions														
28 TOTAL OTHER CASH IN														
29 OTHER CASH OUT														
30 Closing costs														
31 P&I Debt Service	790	790	790	790	790	790	790	790	790	790	790	790	9,480	11.8%
32 Owner Draw	700	700	700	800	800	800	800	800	800	800	800	600	9,100	11.3%
33 Taxes, on Owner Draw														
34 Working capital														
35 Equipment	60	60	60	60	60	60	60	60	60	60	60	60	720	0.9%
36 TOTAL OTHER CASH OUT	(1,550)	(1,550)	(1,550)	(1,650)	(1,650)	(1,650)	(1,650)	(1,650)	(1,650)	(1,650)	(1,650)	(1,450)	(19,300)	-24.1%
37 NET CHANGE IN CASH	1,263	1,161	856	863	1,174	83	(19)	184	(281)	1,401	2,127	1,778	10,590	13.2%
38 BEGINNING CASH	9,798	11,061	12,222	13,078	13,941	15,114	15,197	15,179	15,363	15,083	16,483	18,610	9,798	12.2%
39 ENDING CASH BALANCE	11,061	12,222	13,078	13,941	15,114	15,197	15,179	15,363	15,083	16,483	18,610	20,388	20,388	25.4%

Northeast Entrepreneur Fund, Inc.

These projections present information that is the representation of the business owner/manager for the purpose of business planning, and should not be used for any other purpose. These projections do not include an evaluation of the assumptions or any form of assurance of the achievability of the projections.

CORE FOUR® Business Planning Course, Sample Business Plan, Scrapbook Nook Cash Flow Projections

MARKET PLANNING

C O N T E N T S

THE MASTER PLAN

www.corefouronline.com
1-800-422-0374

Business Plan Blueprint

MARKET PLANNING

Selling   *Pricing*

Promotion   *Image/Packaging*   *Position*

Customers   *Competition*

Distribution   *Product/Service*   *Industry*

WHAT IS MARKETING?

Marketing is meeting a customer's need or want.

WHAT IS A MARKETING PLAN?

A marketing plan is the foundation of a business. It is your written, decisive set of strategies that will position your business in the marketplace to successfully meet customer needs or wants at a profit.

The marketplace is where consumers already purchase nearly anything they want or need, anything you intend to provide. Your business will be part of an existing industry in the marketplace where businesses compete for customers, selling them the products or services you want to sell.

Picture the marketplace as a pie already cut into slices. When an industry is stable or shrinking, your market strategies must be first-rate in order to take customers from existing slices of the pie. In some industries the pie may be growing bigger and only a part of the pie has been cut into slices. When an industry is growing, you have opportunities to slice a piece of the pie for your business. All the while you are in business, you must protect your piece of the pie.

By developing a marketing plan, you will know all about the pie and your share of that pie.

The more you know about the marketplace, the more realistic your market plan will be. Your business will be able to interact in the marketplace effectively, and can respond to market changes with sound market-based strategies.

WHAT DOES THE SUCCESSFUL MARKETING PLAN FOCUS ON?

What is the most important thing your business must absolutely have in order to be a business?

CUSTOMERS!

There is no element more important to your business than customers.

Many people start their businesses believing that their talent or skill will make them successful. There are all kinds of talented, skilled people and wonderful product or service ideas.

Unfortunately, it is not talent, skill, or brilliant ideas that make businesses successful. There are all kinds of mediocre products and services in the marketplace that consumers purchase every day.

The only reason businesses exist is because they have customers.

Businesses are successful when a person, like you, is committed to having a market-driven business.

Have you ever prepared a marketing plan?

If you've ever planned a party, then you've prepared a marketing plan.

When you have a party, you invite a certain group of guests (customers) to get together and have fun (the benefit)! Your party follows a theme consistent with the nature of the event (industry). You plan what to serve (product) and what decorations (packaging) you need. You may provide entertainment or party games (services). You decide where to hold the party (distribution/location). You decide when to hold the party depending on what else is happening (competition). You also send out invitations (promotion) and let people know what they should bring (pricing).

HOW DO YOU BUILD A MARKETING PLAN?

Your marketing plan is the foundation of your business. This foundation consists of the following five layers:

1. Identify your niche – your market position.

a) What are your products/services?
b) What is your distribution process?
c) Who are your customers?
d) What industry are you in?
e) Who is your competition?

Your position (niche) in the marketplace forms the building blocks for all of your subsequent market planning decisions. Your niche helps you identify whether your party is for a wedding with a sit-down dinner for 500 guests, a birthday party for 20 fourth-grade girls, or a quiet, intimate back-yard barbecue at your house for a few close friends.

2. Create an appealing image/package.

The image appropriate for your business will depend on your position in the marketplace. Should you wear a tuxedo to the birthday party? Should you wear your bowling shoes to the wedding? Should the barbecue invitations be gold embossed on white linen paper?

3. Develop a promotional plan.

When you know your market niche and your image, you can design a promotional plan that will reach the right people with the right message at the right time.

Should you advertise on the radio for the wedding? Publish an ad in the newspaper for the birthday party? Drop brochures from a helicopter for the back-yard barbecue?

4. Price your products/services.

Pricing is a market decision, not a personal one. Within the market niche, consumers are prepared to pay based on value. People pay different amounts for wedding gifts than for birthday gifts for 9-year-old girls.

5. Sell your products/services.

If people value what your business offers, it is because you have built relationships within the marketplace. Just as your friends and family will want to come to your party, consumers will want to interact with your business. The selling process is about effectively communicating value.

* * * *

As you can see, the decisions you make about your marketing plan are very much like the decisions you make when planning a party.

So, are you ready to party?

IDENTIFY YOUR PRODUCTS OR SERVICES

WHAT DO YOU SELL? WHAT DO CUSTOMERS BUY?

When identifying your products or services, focus on your customer's need for your product or service, not on your need to sell something. What customer problem are you solving? What is in it for them? What do customers really buy? What is the difference between what you sell or do and what customers buy?

Customers buy *benefits* – not products or services. Think about it: If you wanted to buy a hamburger, you could spend the *time* to go to the grocery store, buy hamburger, take it home, prepare it, cook it; then eat it. When you go to a fast food restaurant to buy a hamburger, you are buying *convenience* rather than the actual hamburger.

WHAT IS A FEATURE?

A feature is a part or piece of your product or service. If your product is a winter coat, the features could be zipper pockets, insulated liner, and detachable hood. If you offer an income tax preparation service, the features could be electronic filing or tax court experience.

WHAT IS A BENEFIT?

When identifying your products or services, think about their benefits to your customers. A benefit is a need or a want. You *need* food, transportation, shelter, and relief from pain. You *want* comfort, appeal, style, charisma, and success.

With the winter coat example, the benefit of the feature *zippered pockets* could be the style or the security of your belongings. The benefit of the feature *insulated liner* could be warmth or comfort. The benefit of the *detachable hood* is extra protection when you need it.

With the tax preparation service example, the feature of electronic filing has a benefit of speedy refund, and the feature of tax court experience has a benefit of offering peace of mind by providing expertise your customers do not have.

People usually want to save or gain something, or they want to be or do something.

The chart below lists examples of benefits – what people want or need to save, gain, be, or do.

Benefits Chart

BENEFITS – PEOPLE WANT OR NEED TO:			
SAVE	**GAIN**	**BE**	**DO**
Time	Health	Good Parents	Express Personalities
Work	Dollars	Sociable	Satisfy Curiosity
Discomfort	Time	Up to Date	Appreciate Beauty
Worries	Popularity	Creative	Acquire Things
Doubts	Security	Attractive	Win Affections
Risks	Prestige	Proud of Their Work	Influence Others
Embarrassment	Praise	Efficient	Improve Themselves
Dollars	Gender Appeal	Comfortable	Advance Their Careers
Energy	Wealth	Important	Leisure Activities
Pain	Relaxation	Winners	Succeed

What benefits could you add to the list?

Next time you watch an ad for tires, notice they sell *safety* rather than the car. Watch a Maytag® commercial. They are selling *dependability* rather than the washing machine. In a Kodak® commercial, aren't they selling *memories* rather than film? How about cellular phone commercials? What benefit are you buying when you buy a cellular phone?

When you watch commercials or read advertisements, think *benefit* and try to identify the benefits being offered, rather than the products or services being featured in the ads.

During your planning process, start with your primary products or services and add new ones in stages as your business plan and your ideas develop. If you work with too many products or services at one time, the business planning process can become complex and overwhelming.

The worksheets on the following pages will help you apply the concepts of:

- **customer wants and needs, and**
- **features and benefits**

to your products and services.

Worksheet—Features and Benefits

1. What customer problems are you solving, or what customer needs or wants are you filling?

2. What future products or services will you offer and when?

Products or Services	By when?

3. List the features and benefits of your primary products or services. (A feature can offer more than one benefit):

Prod/Serv	Features	Benefits
A		
B		
C		
D		

CORE FOUR® Business Planning Course

4. What are the strengths and weaknesses of your primary products or services?

Prod/Serv	Strengths	Weaknesses
A		
B		
C		
D		

5. How are your products produced, or how are your services provided?

6. Who will supply the materials you need to make your product or provide your service?

Prod/Serv	Supplier Name and address	What will they supply?	Payment terms?
A			
B			
C			
D			

7. Why did you select these suppliers? Do you have alternative sources? If so, who are they?

8. When and how often will your customers buy your products or services?
Season? Day of week? Time of day? Every day? Once a month? Once a year?

9. In what other ways could your customers fill their needs or wants instead of buying your products or services?
If you had a telephone answering service, could customers use another service instead?
Use a voicemail service? Hire a receptionist? Let their phone go unanswered? Call forward?

IDENTIFY YOUR DISTRIBUTION PROCESS

You have many options for bringing your product to the marketplace. Your method of distribution, *how you will get your product to the end-user*, will affect every decision hereafter.

Depending on your choice of distribution, your customer (the first person who buys your product or service and **pays you** – the point of sale) can be different than the person who is the end-user of the product or service. However, your customer may not be the actual end-user of the product or service.

If you are selling a service, you usually sell your service directly to the end-user. Sometimes, however, the person who pays you can be different than the end-user of your services. If you are a self-employed home health worker, an insurance company or a county may pay you.

The person who receives your services, the end-user, is the person to whose home you go to provide services.

If you manufacture a product, your customer, the person who pays you, could be an agent, a wholesaler, or a retailer. The end-user, the person who ultimately uses the product, is the customer of the agent, wholesaler, or retailer.

With products, end-users are willing to pay a certain price for your product regardless of whom they buy it from. As you add steps in your distribution chain, each link or business in the chain must charge a higher price to cover its costs.

WHAT ARE YOUR CHOICES OF DISTRIBUTION?

						Advantages	Disadvantages
A	Your Business→				End-User	-Higher selling price -Lower production demands	-Costly/time consuming -Connect with fewer customers
B	Your Business→			Retailer→	End-User		
C	Your Business→		Wholesaler→	Retailer→	End-User	-Fewer customers, more end users -Sell larger quantities	-Lower selling price -Higher production demands
D	Your Business→	Agent→	Wholesaler→	Retailer→	End-User		
E	Your Business→	Agent→		Retailer→	End-User		
Assume:	*Your cost $12*	*Gets 7%*	*Pays $18*	*Pays $30*	*Pays $50*		

The chart above shows the impact of distribution choice on your business.

Let's say you make mittens. The mittens always cost you $12 per pair to make. The end-user, the person who will own and wear the mittens, will pay $50 per pair. No matter who end-users purchase the mittens from, their price will remain at $50.

Example A shows the simplest method of getting your product to the end-user, by selling directly to the end-user, such as at bazaars or craft shows or by direct mail. By selling direct, you gross $38 (50 minus 12) on the sale. Your profit margin is 76% (38 divided by 50). Because you produce and distribute from your home, your operating costs are minimal and you get to keep most of the $38.

Example B is more common form of distribution. If you offered your products for sale in a retail store that you own or lease, the gross from the sale is still $38 and the profit margin is still 76%. However, you have more expenses to pay because you own or lease a store. By the time you are done paying bills you may keep little of the $38 from this type of sale.

Example B would also include selling your products via consignment in another person's store where you would split the sale of the mittens with the storeowner (40% to the store owner and 60% to you). When the end-user buys your mittens for $50, the storeowner gets $20 and you get $30. Your gross from the sale is $18 (30 minus 12), and your profit margin has dropped to 60% (18 divided by 30). You have less money to keep.

Example C shows a typical manufacturer's method of distribution. You make your product and sell it to wholesalers who distribute your product to the marketplace. The end-user should be kept in mind, but your customer is the wholesaler. In this example, you could sell your mittens directly to a supplier of sporting goods stores. You may sell your mittens for $25 to a wholesaler. Your gross from the sale is now $13 (25 minus 12), and your profit margin has dropped to 52% (13 divided by 25).

Example D shows distribution if you hire an agent or manufacturing sales representative to sell for you. You pay the agent a sales commission for making the sale – the agent sells your product to a wholesaler. Your price to the wholesaler may remain the same, $25, but you will have to pay the agent a commission of 7%, or $1.75 per pair of mittens.

The agent may work exclusively for you or may work for many manufacturers. An agent may have the knowledge or contacts that you do not have. In this example, the agent is your first customer.
If the agent does not believe in your product or does not like the way you do business, the agent will not sell your product.

Example E depicts an agent selling your mittens directly to a retailer (a chain of sporting goods stores) instead of to a wholesaler. Again, the agent is your first customer. In this example, your price to the retailer may be $30 and you would pay the agent a commission.

If you have a web site, it may be a method of distribution. If people can order your products from your site, the web site serves as a "retail" site. You would incur costs for order fulfillment and maintenance of the web site.

As the mitten example demonstrates, you have many options for getting your product to the end-user. With each example, your customer is different, the price you get for your mittens is different, and are your cost of doing business is different.

WHAT SHOULD YOU CONSIDER BEFORE CHOOSING YOUR DISTRIBUTION METHOD?

1. The nature of the product. Some products are only meant for direct sale to customers.
2. The size and location of the market. If your marketplace is too far away, it may be best to distribute your products through a wholesaler.
3. The availability of distribution methods. Access to some channels of distribution is limited, and a combination of methods may be required for you to generate your sales goals.
4. The method of distribution used by competition. Could you use a better method, or an existing method in a better way?
5. Your time, energy, money and goals.

The following worksheet will help you evaluate your distribution choices. *If you have more than one method of distribution, copy this worksheet and complete it for each method.*

Worksheet—Distribution

1. Who is your customer? Who is your end-user? In what way are their wants or needs different?

2. Which method of distribution will work best for you? Why?

3. Plot your primary distribution chain:

Your business	Agent	Wholesaler	Retailer	End-User
Your cost	Commission	Pays	Pays	Pays
$	%	$	$	$

$\Rightarrow$

4. What costs are associated with your distribution method?

5. What are possible weak links in your distribution channel?

6. What are possible backup plans if your weakest link fails?

MARKET RESEARCH:
INDUSTRY, CUSTOMERS, AND COMPETITION

WHAT TYPES OF MARKET RESEARCH SHOULD YOU DO?

After you identify your products or services and method of distribution, find out as much as possible about the industry, your customers, and competition. This is the marketplace.

Trends, consumer choices, and competition all change rapidly. These changes will impact your business now and in the future. If you are familiar with the marketplace and how it works, and you stay current with what's happening in the marketplace, you will be able to respond with market strategies when, not if, the marketplace changes.

Since each business is different, the amount of market research needed is different. How much research should you do? As much as possible! The more you know about the industry, customer, and competition, the better you can compete in your marketplace. After all, how can you play the game without knowing all the players and the rules? And how can you stay in the game if you don't know when the players and the rules change?

The following table presents some of the available sources to find out more about your marketplace:

Market Research Chart: Industry, Customers, and Competition

Source	Industry	Customer	Competition
Internet	√	√	√
Yellow Pages	√		√
Encyclopedia of Trade Associations	√	√	√
Trade Publications/Magazines	√	√	
Wholesalers/Suppliers	√	√	
Franchises	√	√	√
Chambers of Commerce	√	√	√
Newspapers	√	√	√
Local economic development agencies	√	√	√
The U.S. Industrial Outlook	√		
Standard and Poor's Industrial Outlook	√		
Risk Management Association	√		
Your Business Competitors	√	√	√
A Guide to Consumer Markets		√	
Census Information		√	
S&MM's Survey of Buying Power		√	
Encyclopedia of Business Information Sources	√	√	√

MARKET RESEARCH SOURCES

You can find many of these sources, including access to the Internet, at your local library. Depending on your business, not all of these sources will have information relevant to your business.

⇒ **Yellow Pages** - Local and other city Yellow Pages may provide the names of your competition as well as names of businesses in other cities that might help you. If you are not sure if your marketplace can support another business like yours, look in the Yellow Pages of a city of comparable size to find out how many businesses are supported in that city. You can also find the Yellow Pages on the Internet.

⇒ **Trade Associations** - Most industries have trade associations that help people better understand their industry and keep you up-to-date on what is happening in your industry. They often have information about your marketplace and research data that you cannot find anywhere else. You can network with other members to get advice and assistance. Many trade associations have web sites on the Internet.

⇒ **Trade Publications** - Some trade associations have publications dedicated to informing business owners on what is happening in their specific marketplace and industry. Sometimes these magazines will research an industry trend or will profile consumer-buying trends.

⇒ **Magazines** - Some magazines will feature articles about people who started similar businesses and how they did it. Most consumer magazines have business feature sections. Some business magazines have Internet versions that you can access online.

⇒ **Wholesalers** - Wholesalers who may purchase your product can give you information about the industry. Because of their experience with the marketplace and end-user, they can give you valuable tips about your product.

⇒ **Suppliers** - Suppliers can be an excellent source of information about costs, potential sales, and customer preferences.

⇒ **Franchises** - You might not have any intention of purchasing a franchise. However, there could be a franchise opportunity that is similar to your business. Sometimes these franchises provide a lot of information about starting your business. Since they have already done much of the work, it is worth investigating what information is available. Information may include customer profiles, startup costs, projected sales, industry trends, or projected expenses. Franchisers may have information about the size of market needed to support your business, or a competitive analysis.

⇒ **Chamber of Commerce** - Most cities have a Chamber of Commerce whose purpose is to help small businesses. These chambers may have statistics on industry trends, population distribution, or buying trends in the area. Many chambers and community organizations have web sites on the Internet.

⇒ **Newspapers** - Many newspapers feature local businesses and their success stories. Most also have business sections that may provide market or opportunity information. Some newspapers have business service directories that will help you find out about local competition who have not advertised in the Yellow Pages. Many newspapers can be searched on the Internet.

⇒ **Business Directories and Other Business Owners** - Business directories list businesses located in your state or across the nation. You can look at these directories from year to year to see if businesses are entering or leaving the marketplace. In addition, you may find other business owners willing to help you.

⇒ **Industry Analysis Books** - *The U.S. Industrial Outlook, Risk Management Association, Standard and Poor's Industrial Outlook*, or the *Market Share Reporter* can give you information about your industry. You can find financial ratios to compare your performance against industry averages.

⇒ **Census Information** - Whether your customer is an individual consumer or a commercial customer, census information can help you determine the size of your targeted market.

⇒ ***Encyclopedia of Business Information Sources*** - This guide is organized by specific topics to help you find additional sources of information that can help you.

⇒ **Other** - There are many other publications available to help you start or expand your business. One of the market research exercises on the following pages provides direction on how to look for these publications.

⇒ **Internet -** The Internet offers a wealth of information. It takes little knowledge and a computer to "surf the net." If you have never done a search on the Internet, check with your local library. Most libraries offer access and some offer training.

⇒ **Local or regional economic development agencies** - These include Small Business Development Centers and other agencies that serve to help with economic development in communities or regions.

⇒ **Licensing agencies** - The Department of Commerce in your state or other department that licenses trades and professions may have information about the trade or profession, particularly the industry that your business is entering.

If you have trouble finding information at your library, ask the reference desk librarian to assist you.

Before beginning your research, review the exercises for your industry, customers, and competition. Depending on your business, not all of these exercises will be necessary, and not everyone can find information about their business in each of these sources.

Your research notes may be critical for validating information you present in a business plan. Worksheets are provided as examples of how to collect data and write down your research results. Use additional sheets or make copies of worksheets where appropriate.

The worksheets on the following pages will help you sort through your market research options.

When you find a worksheet that is not applicable to your business, write *not applicable* and *why you think so* on the worksheet. It will help you remember why you drew the conclusion when someone asks you about the topic.

It will be helpful if you organize your research – perhaps in a file box in file folders by category. You may accumulate a lot of information, including catalogs, lists, customers, and other materials.

Worksheet—Market Research

1. Look in the index of your local Yellow Pages. Write down all of the possible categories you might list your business under. You will use these categories for other research.

2. Using the categories you listed above, search your local Yellow Pages and list all of the businesses that might be your competitors. Use more paper when needed.

Business Name	Address	Phone

3. Using the categories you listed above under question 1, look in another city's Yellow Pages (a city with about the same population and demographics as the city where you will locate your business) and list all the businesses that might be your competitors. Use more paper when needed.

Business Name	Address	Phone

How many similar businesses did you find?	What is the name of the city?	What is the population of the city?

4. Search the *Encyclopedia of Associations, Directory of Associations,* or *National Trade and Professional Associations of the United States Directory* and list any associations that appear to be relevant to your business. If you cannot think of associations important to your business, search for associations to which your customers or suppliers might belong. Write down your findings. Use more paper when needed.

Association Name	Address	Phone

5. Contact trade associations requesting information. Tell them you are doing market research for your business. Ask them questions like:

⇒ What benefits would your business receive by joining their association?

⇒ What market information do they have? Can they refer you to other sources that may have market information? How much does it cost to join?

⇒ Will they provide names and addresses of other members you could contact to find out what they think of the association?

⇒ Does the association offer a trade magazine? Would they mail a sample copy for you to review?

⇒ Does the association have meetings in or near your community? Could you attend a few as a guest before you join?

6. At your local library or online, search the *Reader's Guide to Periodical Literature, Gale Directory of Publications and Broadcast Media*, and periodical section for trade magazines that cover your business or industry. Ask the reference desk librarian for other information about trade publications for your business or industry. Write down your findings. Use more paper when needed.

⇒ Read these publications to see if you can find useful information. Look closely at the advertisements and classifieds. Advertisements can sometimes give you insight into what is happening in your industry.

⇒ Copy any articles that will substantiate information you will include in your business plan about your industry, customers, or competition.

Hint: If you were going to sell reptiles and other exotic animals, you could look under Reptiles, Snakes, or Exotic Animals. Many of these magazines and guides are published quarterly or semi-annually. Look at several issues.

Publication Name	Article Title/Author	Issue Date	Page No.

7. If you are going to sell your product to a wholesaler, your wholesaler can give you useful information about your industry, product, and customers. Look in your library or online for *The American Wholesalers and Distributors Directory* or *The Thomas Register of American Manufacturers*, each of which contains lists of wholesalers.

⇒ Write or call the wholesalers you identify. Tell them you are doing market research for your business and what products you offer. Find out how the wholesalers do business. Do they have any market information for you? Can they help you identify how many of your products you could sell, and to whom?

Wholesaler Name	Address	Phone

8. **If you plan to hire an agent to sell your product, look for the** *Directory of Manufacturer's Sales Agencies* **and list the agents available to sell your product.**

⇒ Write or call the agents you identified. Tell them you are starting or expanding your business and what products or services you offer. Find out how they do business. Do they have market data or helpful hints for you? Can they tell you how many items you might expect to sell and to whom?

Agency Name	Address	Phoned

9. **To find out if a franchise opportunity is available, check the books listed below. They may be available in your library, or you can write directly to the publisher. You also can look under "Franchise" at your library or online to see what other books are available.**

Annual Franchise 500 Entrepreneur Magazine 2445 McCabe Way Irvine, CA 92614 www.entrepreneurmag.com	*Bond's Top 100 Franchises* Robert Bond Source Book Publications 1814 Franklin Street, Suite 820 Oakland, CA 94612 510-839-5471 www.sourcebookpublications.com
Franchising 101 Ann Dugan Upstart Publishing Company, Inc. 12 Portland Street Dover, NH 03820 603-749-5071	*Franchising for Dummies* Michael Seid John Wiley & Sons, Inc. 605 3rd Avenue New York, NY 10158-0012 212-850-6000 www.wiley.com

10. **Contact your local Chamber of Commerce to find out what information is available. You may find your Chamber of Commerce's Directory at your library. In this directory, you will find lists of members who might be potential customers or competitors. You may find business trends or population data that could be useful. You could also look from year-to-year in each directory to see if businesses are entering or leaving the marketplace.**

Potential Customers	Industry Information	Potential Competition

11. **Look at the Business Service Directory in your local newspaper or shopper to find names of possible competitors. Many times, businesses will not advertise in the Yellow Pages because they are new and missed the latest edition, or because they simply chose not to advertise in the telephone book.**

Possible Competitor	Address	Phone

12. Look in your newspaper or search newspapers on the Internet to find feature articles on similar businesses. Sometimes you can find these feature articles in other cities' newspapers. Your librarian can help you with your search and help you find back issues of newspapers.

Name of Business or Article	Publication Name	Publication Date	Page No.

13. Learn all you can about your industry. Find either or both of the following books at your library: *Standard and Poor's* and the *Market Share Reporter*. Look in the front of each of these books to understand the types of information they offer. Look under the subject/industry that applies to your business. Make copies of these pages of information for future reference.

Did all of your sources have the same outlook? What is the general outlook?

Is the industry growing, declining, or changing? In what way?

14. Measure your actual or projected financial performance against the industry average. To do this, go to your library and look for *Almanac of Business and Industrial Financial Ratios* or *RMA – Risk Management Association's Annual Statements* under your industry classification. Copy the pages that apply to your business type. Also copy the first few pages in the book that explain what each financial ratio means and how they are calculated.

⇒ Compare your projected profit margin to your industry average profit margin. This ratio will tell you what percent of your sales should be your profit. For example, if you are starting a flower shop, the industry profit margin is approximately 4%. This means for every $100 of sales, you make $4 (after all expenses but before taxes). If you are starting a real estate office, the industry profit margin is approximately 10%. This means for every $100 of commission, you make $10 (after all expenses but before taxes).

⇒ Each industry and business will have different expenses. By comparing your business to industry averages, you will learn if you are reasonably projecting the finances of your business.

15. To find other sources of useful information for business, go to your library and locate the *Small Business Source* book or the *Encyclopedia of Business Information Sources*. These books will tell you about associations, newsletters, magazines, and other books about your industry. This comprehensive guide is arranged by subject. Look under the subject that applies to your business and copy all the pages showing the available resources. Locate these and other resources in your library and research what information they have to help you.

Your research notes:

16. Your customers are the key to success for your business. You must understand their needs and wants. Locate the following books at your library and copy any information that may help you understand who your customers are, what they want or need, how to find them, how they make choices, what they read – anything and everything you can learn.

⇒ *Survey of Buying Power* - This guide provides current figures on population and demographics, effective buying income, and customer spending patterns. It contains information on retail sales and market quality indexes for state, county, city, and metro markets - everything you need for targeting potential customers in all geographic areas.

⇒ *How Customers Think – Essentials for the Mind of the Market* by Gerald Zaltman

Your research notes:

17. Obtain and copy any and all census and demographic information about your geographic market. You will use this information when completing your customer profile, target market, and number of potential customers.

⇒ Census information can be used to estimate the size of your targeted market. Let's say your target market is women between the ages of 25 and 50 who make more than $30,000 per year and live in your city. You can find the number of women who fit this description from census information. The library has census information, or use www.census.gov.

⇒ Many community agencies have Internet web sites with this type of data.

⇒ The *Source Book of Zip Code Demographics, 2003* published by ESRI Business Information Systems lists census information by city and also includes some buying power indexes.

⇒ A book titled *Demographics of the U.S.: Trends and Projections* by Charles Russell contains demographic information, trends, and projections.

Your research notes:

18. At your library, look under the subject that describes your business type (refer to the categories you listed in Exercise 1). For example, if you are starting a deli, you could look under Restaurants, Deli, Catering, or Food Businesses. Look for every book on your subject. You may find a book that tells you all you need to know about starting your specific business. At a minimum, find any book about your subject matter.

Name of Book or Article	Publication Name/Author	Publication Date	Page No.

19. Contact as many other business owners as possible. These people can be your greatest resource. Their experience, knowledge, and expertise cannot be duplicated in any book.

If you had the chance to ask an experienced business owner any question about starting your business, what would you ask? You may be surprised how willing other business owners are to talk to you. Many will feel flattered by your asking them for their expertise.

♦ Make a list of the questions you would like to ask. A sample questionnaire is on the following page. Ask your questions in order of importance since you may only get to ask a few of them. Make copies of this or your own questionnaire so you have one for each business you contact.

♦ Call the business first to find out the owner's name. You could write the business owner a letter explaining how you got their name and that you are starting a similar business in another city. This may erase any fears the business owner may have about you being a competitor in the same marketplace. Let them know you would like to talk to them and ask a few questions because you value their experience.

♦ Always make an appointment to visit in person or by phone – don't drop by or phone and expect someone to be willing to spend time. Call to let them know how you got their name and why you are calling. The business owner will probably tell you more if you meet in person rather than over the phone.

♦ When you call the owner, thank them for taking your call. Ask them if this is a convenient time to talk, or if you should set up another time to call back. You should have your questions ready so you do not waste the owner's time. This will make sure you get your most important questions answered.

♦ At the end of every interview, thank the owner for his or her time and help. Send a thank you note as well. If the business owner was receptive to helping you, keep that in mind for future help once you have started your business.

♦ You will meet many individuals who do not want to help you and may even be rude. Do not let them discourage you – maybe they are having a bad day. Do not take it personally. It is common to feel self-conscious and unsure of yourself when talking with a stranger, but remember, they probably feel the same way. After all, you are a stranger to them, too.

♦ Open-ended questions, to which the answer cannot be yes or no, are best to ask. If you ask, "Do you have any advice for me?" the answer could be a simple "no." If you ask, "What would you do differently to start your business today?" it is likely you will get a more descriptive answer than "nothing" or "everything."

Questionnaire—For Interviewing a Business Owner

A sample questionnaire for interviewing a business is provided below. You can use the same questions as are on this form, or you can think of your own questions. Think about the *answers* and *information* that will be helpful to you, and then create the questions. Be sure to prioritize your questions in order of importance to you – you may only get the opportunity to ask two or three questions, so you want to be sure to focus on the ones that are most important.

It will be helpful for you to practice interviewing a business owner. Ask a friend or family member to help you. Trade roles – you can be the interviewer in the first practice session, and the business owner in the second practice session. This will give you an opportunity to think about how it will feel to be on either side of the conversation, and will rehearse you to feel comfortable during an actual interview.

			Date contacted
Person contacted	**Business name**	**Business address**	

How long have you been in business? *Since most businesses fail within the first two to five years, this might give you an indication of how successful this business has been.*
How many employees do you have? *This will let you know the size of their operation. If they have 50 employees and you plan to have only a few, then their suggestions may not fit your business.*
Who are your customers? *This may help you with your customer profile information.*
How did you get started? *Business owners might share their bad experiences or mistakes. Sometimes it is more important to find out what **not** to do, rather than what to do.*
What type of advertising has worked best for you? *This may help you when planning your promotional plan.*
Is the business seasonal? If so, when is the busiest time? *This information will help you when preparing your cash flow.*
What do you wish you would not/would have done if you could do it over again?
Additional questions:

IDENTIFY YOUR INDUSTRY

What is happening in your industry? Have there been any new developments that might give you a competitive advantage? Is technology changing the industry? In what way?

Worksheet—Industry

1. Is the industry growing, shrinking, or stable? How do you know?

2. Are companies entering or leaving the marketplace? How do you know?

3. Is the industry different in your region or area compared to what is happening nationally? If so, why, and what impact will it have on your sales or costs?

4. Have there been any changes in the industry? If so, what impact did they have?

5. How do you think technology will impact the industry in the future? Why?

6. What trade associations are available for businesses in this industry?

Association Name	Address	Phone

7. Are there fees to join or participate? If so, how much and when do you need to pay them?

	Monthly	Quarterly	Annually
Membership fee	$	$	$
Meeting fees (lunch costs, etc.)	$	$	$
Subscription fee for association magazine or newsletter	$	$	$
Other (describe)	$	$	$

8. How do these associations support or work with the industry? How do you think they would or would not be helpful to your business?

IDENTIFY YOUR CUSTOMERS

WHO ARE YOUR CUSTOMERS?

Who purchases your products or services from you and *pays* you?

Think about your answers to the following questions:

1. Who are your customers?
2. What benefits do your customers want or need?
3. What quantities will they buy?
4. How often will they buy?
5. What are they willing to pay?
6. Why will they buy from you instead of someone else?
7. How many customers will you have?

TARGET YOUR IDEAL CUSTOMERS

Different types of customers have different types of buying habits.

The 80/20 rule-of-thumb of marketing is that 80% of your sales are likely sold to 20% of your customers. If you have 100 customers, then 20 of those customers spend the most money with you most often, and make up the majority of your total sales.

You will benefit by understanding those 20 customers so you can keep them and find more customers just like them. While the 80/20 rule is a generalization, it is likely that a minority of your customers will account for the majority of your sales.

Your business should focus on the target group of customers to do business with since the target group has focused on your business.

In order to focus on the target group, develop a customer profile of your targeted customer.

The worksheets on the following pages will help you understand the needs and wants of your customers.

If you are starting a new business and will sell to:

- the individual consumer who is an end-user, complete Section A on the following pages.

- a wholesaler, distributor, agent, or commercial customer, complete Section B on the following pages.

If you already have a business, complete Section C on the following pages.

If you have a mix of customers types, review Sections A, B, and C and complete each appropriate section.

SECTION A—INDIVIDUAL CUSTOMERS

Individual consumers can be grouped by demographic characteristics of people, such as age, gender, occupation, and income. It is important to know the common traits your customers share. If you know their common traits, you can target your promotional efforts more effectively.

Some of the more common traits include:

Gender – Each gender has different buying habits. Knowing if your market is mostly male, female, or a mix of gender, is fundamental to your marketing plan.

Age – Different age groups have significantly different buying habits and interests.

Income – In addition to wanting to buy your products or services, your customer must have the ability to pay for them.

Geographic location – Whether by neighborhood, zip code, city, state, or shopping area, many businesses discover most of their business comes from specific locations rather than from all over town.

Occupation – Buying capabilities and buying habits may be different if your customer is a blue-collar laborer or a white-collar professional.

Other – Lifestyle, marital status, number of dependents, and interests or hobbies can influence buying habits. These characteristics are more difficult to track, but can give you great insight into your customer's needs and wants.

Consider doing a customer survey. Review the survey on the next page to develop and conduct your own survey. You can conduct your survey in person, over the phone, or by mail. After completing your survey, you can develop a customer profile.

You might want to sell or give samples of your product or service to customers, then conduct a survey. You will find their answers will be even more helpful if your customers have actually used your product or are familiar with your services.

One of your primary objectives is to determine what your customers have in common. Why? So you can more effectively aim your promotional strategies at your targeted group of customers.

There are also various *categories* of customers. You might have individual, industrial/commercial, or government customers – each category requiring different services or products. You also must consider *existing* customers of various types. If there are files on current customers, you can find helpful data there. Most businesses have more than one category of customers.

Worksheets for identifying individuals who will be your customers are on the following pages.

Individual Customer Needs Survey

To help us evaluate our [product] [services] we seek the opinions of customers like yourself. Please answer the questions below.

Gender	Annual Income*	Age	
__Male	__Under $10,000	__13-17	Your zip code_____
	__$11,000 to $30,000	__18-24	
__Female	__$31,000 to $50,000	__25-34	Your occupation_____
	__Over $50,000	__35-49	
		__50-55	
		__over 55	
	*optional		

1. Do you ever purchase this [product] [service] ? __Yes __No Why or why not?

2. Using the scale: 1=very important, 2=somewhat important, 3= not important, please rate the following about this [product] [service]:

1-2-3		1-2-3		1-2-3	
	Quality		Customer service		Service after sale
	Availability		Location of store		
	Price		On time delivery		

3. What is the one thing you like most about this [product] [service]?

4. How do you think the [product] [service] should be improved?

5. If these improvements were made, would you be willing to pay more for the [product] [service]?

   If yes, how much more?

6. How often do you [buy] [use] this [product] [service]?

7. From whom do you buy this [product] [service]?

8. How much do you usually pay for the [product] [service]?

9.

10.

Worksheet—Individual Customer Profile

1. Research your *individual* customer profile.

Using the table below, record how your customers fit into each demographic you identify as important to your business. Create other demographic categories as needed for your business.

2. Identify your *composite individual* customer profile.

On the chart below, List the *largest group* from each category that you identified on the chart on the left.

Gender	Number	Percent
Male		
Female		
Total		100%
Annual Income		
Under $10,000		
11 to 30		
31 to 50		
over 50		
Total		100%
Age		
13-17		
18-24		
25-34		
35-49		
50-55		
55+		
Total		100%
Occupation		
Admin/clerical		
Blue collar		
Professional		
Retired		
Student		
Other		
Totals		100%
Zip Codes		
1		
2		
3		
4		
Totals		100%

Gender	Number	Percent
Male		
Female		
Annual Income		
Under $10,000		
11 to 30		
31 to 50		
over 50		
Age		
13-17		
18-24		
25-34		
35-49		
50-55		
55+		
Occupation		
Admin/clerical		
Blue collar		
Professional		
Retired		
Student		
Other		
Zip Codes		
1		
2		
3		
4		

3. Verify your original assumptions about your customers. You answered the following questions earlier. Now that you have researched your customers, are your answers still the same?

a) Who are your customers?

b) What benefits do your customers want or need?

c) What quantities will they buy?

d) How often will they buy?

e) When will they buy (season, time of day, week, month, year)?

f) What are they willing to pay?

g) Why will they buy from you instead of someone else?

h) How many customers will you have?

CORE FOUR® Business Planning Course

SECTION B—
COMMERCIAL/INDUSTRIAL CUSTOMERS

Commercial or industrial customers can be grouped by demographics such as industry classification, number of employees, or annual sales volume. It is important to know the common traits your customers share so you can target your promotional efforts more effectively. Some of the more common traits include the following:

Private vs. Public/Government – Whether your customer is a private company or a public or government agency will greatly impact the way you interact with that customer. Government agencies have a different approach to doing business than commercial customers. They usually require bids before awarding contracts. Regardless if your customer is private or public, the way they pay also needs to be determined since it will impact your cash flow.

Industry Classification – Depending on the industry, your customers will do business differently. Some industries have more conservative buying habits. With each different industry, you will find different needs depending on what is happening in their industry.

Number of Employees – Size of a company is sometimes determined by the number of people employed by that company.

Annual Sales Volume – May indicate a company's ability to purchase your product, or how much or how often they might purchase.

Geographic Location – Geographic location of your customers will impact your cost to deliver to customers.

Worksheets for identifying commercial and industrial customers are on the following pages.

Worksheet—Commercial/Industrial Customer Profile

1. **Research your *commercial/industrial* customer profile.**

Using the table below, record how your customers fit into each demographic category you identify as important to your business. Create other demographic categories as needed for your business.

2. **Identify your *composite commercial/industrial* customer profile.**

On the chart below, List the *largest group* from each category that you identified on the chart on the left.

	Number	Percent
Commercial		
Public/Govt		
Totals		100%
Industry		
Retail		
Construction		
Banking		
Totals		100%
Employees		
1-25		
26-100		
101-250		
251-500		
over 500		
Totals		100%
Annual sales (k=$1,000)		
up to $50k		
50k to 100k		
100K to 250K		
250K to 500K		
500k to 1,000k		
1,000k +		
Totals		100%
Zip Codes		
1		
2		
3		
4		
5		
Totals		100%

	Number	Percent
Commercial		
Public/Govt		
Industry		
Retail		
Construction		
Banking		
Employees		
1-25		
26-100		
101-250		
251-500		
over 500		
Annual sales (k=$1,000)		
up to $50k		
50k to 100k		
100K to 250K		
250K to 500K		
500k to 1,000k		
1,000k +		
Zip Codes		
1		
2		
3		
4		
5		

3. Verify your original assumptions about your customers. You answered the following questions earlier. Now that you have researched your customers, are your answers still the same?

a) Who are your customers?

b) What benefits do your customers want or need?

c) What quantities will they buy?

d) How often will they buy?

e) When will they buy (season, time of day, week, month, year)?

f) What are they willing to pay?

g) Why will they buy from you instead of someone else?

h) How many customers will you have?

SECTION C—EXISTING BUSINESSES—CUSTOMER PROFILE

If you already have a business, you already have customers. What do you really know about them?

To develop your customer profile, read Section A or Section B, depending on your type of customer, to understand more about demographics.

Ideally, you could get most of this information from your customer files.

You can also survey your customers to find out what they really want or need (it may be different than what you want to sell to them). A survey can also be a promotional tool to let your customers know that what they think is important to you.

Use the appropriate sample survey on the following pages, depending on your type of customer.

You can survey your customers in person or by mail with a letter of explanation. If you choose to mail your survey, include a self-addressed, stamped envelope to increase the number of responses.

Then go back to Section A or Section B, depending on your type of customer, and define your customer profile.

Satisfaction Survey—Individual Customer

In our continuous effort to improve the quality of service we provide, we seek the honest opinions of customers like you. Please take a minute to answer the questions below.

Gender	Annual Income*	Age	
__Male	__Under $10,000	__13-17	Your zip code_____
	__$11,000 to $30,000	__18-24	
__Female	__$31,000 to $50,000	__25-34	Your occupation_____
	__Over $50,000	__35-49	
		__50-55	
		__over 55	
	*optional		

1. Using the scale: 1=Excellent, 2=Average, 3= Poor, please rate the following about our company:

1-2-3		1-2-3		1-2-3	
	Quality		Customer service		Variety
	Availability		Location of store		Service after sale
	Price		On time delivery		

2. What is the one thing you like most about our company?

3. What could we do to improve that would be helpful for you?

4. How often do you [shop here, buy use] our [product] [service]?

5. How much do you usually spend when you shop with us?

6. Why do you buy from us rather than someone else?

7. What else could we provide for you that we presently do not have or offer?

8. When you don't buy from us, who do you buy from? Why?

9.

10.

Satisfaction Survey—Commercial/Industrial Customers

In our continuous effort to improve the quality of service we provide, we seek the honest opinions of customers like you. Please take a minute to answer the questions below.

Number of Employees	Annual Sales Range	Industry Classification	Zip Code

1. Using the scale: 1=Excellent, 2=Average, 3= Poor, please rate the following about our company:

1-2-3		1-2-3		1-2-3	
	Quality		Customer service		Variety
	Availability		Location of store		Service after sale
	Price		On time delivery		

2. What is the one thing you like most about our company?

3. What could we do to improve that would be helpful for you?

4. How often do you [shop here, buy use] our [product] [service]?

5. How much do you usually spend when you shop with us?

6. Why do you buy from us rather than someone else?

7. What else could we provide for you that we presently do not have or offer?

8. When you don't buy from us, who do you buy from? Why?

9.

10.

IDENTIFY YOUR COMPETITION

WHO ARE YOUR COMPETITORS?

Your competitors are those businesses that sell products or services similar to yours, to the same targeted customers as yours, and generally distribute in ways similar to you.

When you know how you will get your products to the marketplace (distribution) and who your customers are (target market), find out as much as you can about your competitors.

Worksheet—Competitive Analysis

1. **Insert the names and addresses of your three main competitors:**

COMPETITOR A		
Name	Address	Phone
COMPETITOR B		
Name	Address	Phone
COMPETITOR C		
Name	Address	Phone

2. **Conduct a competitor evaluation.**

Evaluate each competitor listed using criteria defined on the following page. A blank evaluation worksheet is on page 37-MP.

Read through the definitions to understand what you are trying to evaluate. Add or delete criteria as appropriate.

Go shopping! See what your competitors have to offer. Write down your observations about each of the categories.

If you cannot visit the competition because they know who you are, have a friend or a relative, whose judgment you trust, perform the evaluation.

When visiting your competition, look at the types of customers buying the product. If you do not know much about your customer, you can learn more about them through your observations. Do they seem happy with the products or services they buy? If you find that your competitor is serving an entirely different set of customers (target market) then that business may not be your competitor. If so, evaluate another competitor.

3. **Assess your competitors' promotional efforts.**

This includes business cards, newspaper ads, brochures, catalogs, store layout, and any other promotional strategies.

4. **After you have evaluated the competition, complete the evaluation worksheet for your business.**

COMPETITOR EVALUATION CRITERIA

While you may not use all the categories defined below, evaluate as many as you can. If there are other categories that are more important, include them on your form.

Product – Which product does the better job?

Product Selection – How many choices do the customers have? Can customers meet all their needs/wants by doing business with you?

Quality – How long does the product last? How well is it made? If you offer a service, do you do a thorough job?

Availability – Are the products always available? How many hours are you open?

Warranty – Do you offer any warranty? Do you replace or repair defective parts?

Expertise – How much experience do you have in making the product? Are you skilled at it? If you offer a service, do you have experience and knowledge related to your area of service?

Service after the sale – What is done to assure customer satisfaction? Does your business provide service after the sale, or does the manufacturer? Do you contract for this service with another vendor? What are their reputations?

Reputation – What do customers think of you and your company? Do they know what you do?

Image/Appearance – What does your packaging look like? Does it fit your image? What does your store/office look like? What do *you* look like? Do you dress appropriately for the job? Does your appearance match your image?

Location – Is your office/store located near your customers? Is there adequate parking? Is your sign large enough to get your customers' attention? Is your office/store visible? Is your location easy to get to?

Customization – Are you willing to change your products or services to meet a special customer need?

Reliability – Do your products require too much repair or service? If you offer a service, can the customer depend on you to do a complete, timely, and correct job?

Credit Policy – What types of payment will you accept? Do you accept credit cards? If you offer your own credit, what are your terms and interest rate?

Management – How well does management take care of business? Does management take care of its employees?

Customer Service – Are customers treated well? Are employees courteous and friendly? Do customers have to wait? Do employees help customers find what they are looking for?

Advertisement – What forms of advertisement are used?

Type of Customers – Who is buying the products? Do they have anything in common? Which target market are you serving?

Price – How much does the product cost? Is the product overpriced or underpriced?

Competitor Evaluation Worksheet

Competitor's Name:

	Items Rated	Comments	1-10
1.	Product		
2.	Selection		
3.	Quality		
4.	Availability		
5.	Hours		
6.	Warranties		
7.	Expertise		
8.	Service after sale		
9.	Reputation		
10.	Image/appearance		
11.	Location		
12.	Special orders		
13.	Reliability		
14.	Credit policy		
15.	Management		
16.	Customer service		
17.	Advertisement		
18.	Customer type		
19.	Price		
What is their greatest strength?			
What is their greatest weakness?			
What types of promotion do they use?			
Does the promotion attract your attention? If so, how?			
Do they regularly promote in the same way?			
What is the primary value offered?			

Competitor Evaluation Worksheet 2

Competitor's Name:

	Items Rated	Comments	1-10
20.	Product		
21.	Selection		
22.	Quality		
23.	Availability		
24.	Hours		
25.	Warranties		
26.	Expertise		
27.	Service after sale		
28.	Reputation		
29.	Image/appearance		
30.	Location		
31.	Special orders		
32.	Reliability		
33.	Credit policy		
34.	Management		
35.	Customer service		
36.	Advertisement		
37.	Customer type		
38.	Price		

What is their greatest strength?	
What is their greatest weakness?	
What types of promotion do they use?	
Does the promotion attract your attention? If so, how?	
Do they regularly promote in the same way?	
What is the primary value offered?	

POSITION YOUR PRODUCTS/SERVICES

FIND YOUR MARKET NICHE

Once you know all about your competition, you can **position** them in the marketplace. Then you can identify your position, your niche, in the marketplace.

Once you know where your competitors are in the marketplace in relationship to your business, you may find:

- a gap that no one is serving, or

- your competition is very strong in the niche you wish to compete in.

You could consider going after an opportunity in a gap in the marketplace, or identifying another position in which you could compete.

1. Rate your competitive evaluations.

Using the competitor evaluations you prepared, rate your observations in each of the evaluation categories.

Rate each observation on a scale from 1 to 10, 1 being poor and 10 being excellent.

For example, if a competitor has terrible customer service, then rate that observation as 1. If a competitor has an excellent reputation, then rate that observation as 10. If a competitor does not offer credit, then rate that observation as 0. If no one offers credit, including your business, then take that observation off the evaluation chart.

2. Prepare a Competitor Evaluation Worksheet for your business.

Rate your business to determine where you fit in the marketplace.

Be honest with yourself! Your objective is to determine gaps or opportunities that your competitors are not serving. Sometimes where you want to be and where you end up in the marketplace can be different things. If this turns out to be the case, you can make changes to your plan so that you get to where you want to be.

If you are a new company, you may not have an image or reputation. Rate that observation as 0.

3. Calculate the average score for each competitor and your business.

Divide the total score for each business evaluated (including yours), by the total number of observations.

4. Use the scores to plot your market position in relationship to your competitors.

A case example of the positioning exercises using flower shops is on the following pages. For the purpose of this example, the competitive analyses are depicted on a table. For your research, you would have a single form for each competitor as well as for your business.

Review the example before you do these market position exercises. Remember – pricing is an art and a science. The art is market strategy and the science is cash flow planning.

Example—Competitive Analysis Chart—Flower Shops

	Items Rated	Competitor A Grocery Store	1 to 10	Competitor B Granny's Floral	1 to 10
1.	Product	n/a	—	n/a	—
2.	Selection	very limited	2	fair selection	4
3.	Quality	wilt quickly	2	do not last	2
4.	Availability	not always in stock	1	limited selection	4
5.	Hours	7 am to 9 pm every day		10 am to 5pm Mon-Fri, Sat 9 am to noon	
6.	Warranties	n/a	—	n/a	—
7.	Expertise	not trained in floral arrangements	0	some arrangement experience	4
8.	Service after sale	no returns or replacements	0	replaced if within one day of purchase	4
9.	Reputation	not very well known as a source of flowers	3	variety, but not consistent quality	4
10.	Image/appearance	kiosk display is messy and cluttered	3	cute store, attractive displays	6
11.	Location	good location	7	out of way in residential area	2
12.	Special orders	pre-packaged only	0	displayed items only	0
13.	Reliability	n/a	—	n/a	—
14.	Credit policy	cash or check only	0	cash or check only	0
15.	Management	kiosk refilled weekly, wilted flowers remain in stock	2	offers sales, stock well maintained and fresh	5
16.	Customer service	none other than at checkout	4	only 1 employee and often have to wait	2
17.	Advertisement	does not promote flowers at all	0	runs ads in weekly shopper	
18.	Customer type		0		
19.	Price	$3.00 per rose		$5.00 per rose	
20.	Delivery		0		0
21.	Wire service		0		0
22.					
23.					
24.	Price	$3.00 per rose		$5.00 per rose	
	Total Scores		24		37
	Number of categories rated		14		14
	Average Score = Total score divided by number of categories rated		1.71		2.64
	Greatest strength	Location, convenience, pick up flowers while you shop		Cute store, has lots of charm	
	Greatest weakness	Poor selection and quality, no delivery or wire service		Out of-way location, not best quality of flowers	

Competitor C Flowers Are Us	1 to 10	YB Your Floral Business	1 to 10
n/a	—		
wide variety	7		10
fresh flowers last about a week	7		7
most are available but some are special ordered	6		9
10 am to 5pm Mon-Fri, Sat 9 am to noon			
n/a	—	n/a	—
good arrangement experience	6		9
no returns or replacements	2		8
variety and quality, poor customer service	4		0
Well-lighted, good displays	6		8
good location	5		6
custom orders on request	7		9
n/a	—		
cash, check, or credit card	5		10
Well-run business but poor customer satisfaction	5		9
employees are rude and always "too busy"	2		10
ads in local paper and local billboard			
$7.00 per rose		To be determined	
	8		8
	5		8
$7.00 per rose			
	75		111
	14		14
	5.36		7.93
Product selection, quality, experience			
Customer service and customer satisfaction			

Worksheet—Marketplace Position – Flower Shops Part 1

With the flower shops competitive analysis chart on the preceding pages as an example, how you would plot everyone's position on the market position chart?

	Company A	Company B	Company C	Company YB Your Business
Average Score	1.71	2.64	5.35	7.9
Price of Rose	$3.00	$5.00	$7.00	Undetermined

Average Score	PRICE									
	$2	$3	$4	$5	$6	$7	$8	$9	$10	$11
1										
2		A								
3				B						
4										
5						C				
6										
7										
8	YB	YB	YB	YB	YB	YB	YB	YB	YB	YB
9										
10										

The dark shaded areas represent areas of the marketplace that you **cannot** enter. Customers typically will not pay the same price for less service, nor will they pay more for the same level of service.

Now you can evaluate your alternatives. YB represents your overall observations score.

The light shaded areas represent areas of the marketplace you **should not** have to enter. If people are already willing to pay a certain price for an existing level of service, you should not charge less for your service.

The white areas represent your options. If you offer more, you should charge more. In order to charge more, you must educate your customers about the benefits you offer. When customers understand what they are paying for, they are usually willing to pay a higher price. Once you understand where your competition is located, you can review your options and decide where you want to be in the marketplace.

Example—Marketplace Position Worksheet – Flower Shops Part 2

Average Score	PRICE									
	$2	$3	$4	$5	$6	$7	$8	$9	$10	$11
1										
2		A								
3				B						
4										
5						C				
6										
7										
8	YB	YB	YB	YB	YB	YB	YB	YB	YB	YB
9										
10										

Competitor Evaluation Summary Worksheet

	Items Rated	Competitor A	Competitor B	Competitor C	Your Business
1.	Product				
2.	Selection				
3.	Quality				
4.	Availability				
5.	Hours				
6.	Warranties				
7.	Expertise				
8.	Service after sale				
9.	Reputation				
10.	Image/appearance				
11.	Location				
12.	Special orders				
13.	Reliability				
14.	Credit policy				
15.	Management				
16.	Customer service				
17.	Advertisement				
18.	Customer type				
19.	Price				
20.	Delivery				
21.					
22.					
23.					
24.					
	Total Scores				
Number of categories rated					
Average Score = Total score divided by number of categories rated					
Greatest strength					
Greatest weakness					

Market Position Worksheet

After finding an average score for you and your competitors, plot everyone's position on the marketplace chart.

Write the price ranges across the top of the chart. Working from left to right, start with the lowest price and finish with the highest price. Then, under the appropriate price column, find the row that matches that competitor's average score. Find where the column and row intersect and place the name of that competitor in that box. Follow the example for Flower Shops on the previous pages.

Average Score	PRICE											
1												
2												
3												
4												
5												
6												
7												
8												
9												
10												

1. What are your competitive advantages? What makes you unique from your competition?

Place a √ next to the items that will be your competitive advantage.

	Most reliable		Best warranty		?
	Most convenient		Best location		?
	Best service after sale		Best credit policy		?
	Most unusual		Best customer service		?
	Most expertise		Best reputation		?
	Best selection		Highest quality		?

2. What changes will you make to improve your position in the marketplace?

CREATE AN APPEALING IMAGE/PACKAGE

WHAT IS PACKAGING?

Packaging is any way your customer sees or comes into contact with you, your product, or your business.

Your customers' opinions can be influenced positively or negatively by your image or packaging. You don't get a second chance to make a first impression!

Have you ever been in a restaurant and seen dirty floors, tables, or dishes? What did you think? Would you buy an olive green and carnation pink sports car? Would you hire a lawyer to represent your interests in a lawsuit if the lawyer handed you a business card that was handwritten on a piece of paper? Would you hire a general contractor who wore ripped, dirty clothes and smelled like a sweaty locker room to remodel your kitchen?

WHY IS PACKAGING SO IMPORTANT?

Successful advertising agencies recognize the importance of packaging. Some even live by the old advertising adage:

- color catches the eye,
- styling makes them buy,
- performance makes them cry or re-buy.

Individual consumers and commercial customers value things differently. The following chart shows the order of importance of preferences for each type of customer. While the order of these preferences might not always hold up, you should keep it in mind.

ORDER OF IMPORTANCE	INDIVIDUAL CONSUMER	COMMERCIAL CUSTOMER
1	Style	Performance
2	Color	Style
3	Performance	Color

We all are affected to some degree by how products and service providers look. Think about the things you buy, who you buy them from and *why* you buy the things you do. Think about the businesses you buy from and *why* you buy from them. Use your own experiences and what you learned from your competition when creating an image for your business.

WHAT TYPES OF PACKAGING ISSUES SHOULD YOU ADDRESS?

Your packaging may make or break a sale. The following list describes the different types of packaging decisions you should address. Think of your position in the marketplace and package your business accordingly.

You! Your dress, hygiene, and speech – Dress for your customers. Customers will make judgments about your business based on your appearance. Make sure that your clothes are clean and that you are well-groomed. Personal hygiene is a must – clean hair, clean hands, and fresh breath all make you feel better. Dressing for success will not only make you feel better, it will make a better impression on your customer.

Customer Reception/Phone Greeting – The way customers are greeted when they come in your office or store will give them an instant impression about you and your business. Customers should not be ignored, that's obvious. But so many businesses ignore the importance of customer service. The way you answer your phone can make or break a sale. Everyone who answers your business phone should answer your phone professionally. If you have a home-based business, show your children how to answer the business line professionally. A customer will not get a good impression if your child screams, "*MOM/DAD, THE PHONE'S FOR YOU!*"

Carton or Wrapping – If your product needs a carton or wrapping, the look of the package itself can motivate a customer to buy your product instead of another product. Try to make your carton look appealing. Use the following information when designing your package.

Product Style – Some products are more enticing because of their style. You can make your products look old-fashioned, conventional, or modern. You can design and make your product in accord with a prevailing fashion. Depending on the image you are trying to convey, pick the best style to convey that image.

Name, Subtitle, Slogan – When selecting the name for your business, the business name should let potential customers know what type of products or services you offer. Let's say you are starting your own sign-making business and your name is Ron Jenson. If you call your business **Jenson Enterprises**, your potential customers will have no idea what your company does when they see your company name. However, if you call your business **Jenson Signs**, your customers will know what type of services you offer.

If you already have a business and your business name does not let people know what you do, you could add a subtitle or slogan under your name to let people know. If your business name was Jenson Enterprises, you could add a subtitle of *Maker of Fine Signs* to let people know more about your business. You also could add a slogan as one sign company did: *A business without a sign is a sign of no business.*

Location – If you require an office or retail store, think carefully about its location. Again, think about the customer. Where does the customer live, work, or shop? Is there enough parking for the customer's convenience? Will you be located next to other stores or offices the customer might use?

Office/Store Layout – How your office or store looks will affect your customers. If you have an office, design your decor with your customers' comfort in mind. Your customers should feel comfortable and welcome. If you have a store, the floor plan or store layout can affect your customers. Display your products attractively. Are products located logically and conveniently?

Logo – Logos can be helpful for recognition and recall. As the old saying goes, "a picture is worth a thousand words." Your logo lets your customers know what your business does with a picture that relates to the nature of your business. If you use a logo, pick a logo that makes sense.

Let's say you are an electrician. Which of the following logos makes more sense to your customers, Logo A or B?

A   B

It depends! You could use either depending on the type of electrical work you perform. If you

focus on installing telephone wire in commercial buildings, logo A would be better than logo B. If you rewire old homes, logo B would be better than logo A.

Color – Color can enhance your image. Color also can catch your customers' attention. If you are opening an automobile repair garage, a pastel pink color on the walls would give a different impression than a royal blue color. Not everyone will agree on what each color conveys, but the following list will help you think about it.

Gold, Silver, Royal Blue – quality and reliability
Purple – regal, intrigue
Green – tranquility, nature, dollars, environment
Blue – tranquility, calmness
Orange, yellow – warmth, happiness, comfort
Red – fire, heat, excitement
Pastels – femininity
Brown, Black – masculine, sadness, ominous
Neons – excitement, trendy

Typestyle – Typestyle is the type of lettering you choose for your business name. Typestyles, like colors, also convey certain meanings. The following is an example of how typestyles can work for you, or against you.

GEORGE'S GARAGE

Make the most of your image by selecting a typestyle suited to your business. Then use that typestyle for *everything* published by your business.

Business Cards and Stationery – Design your business card and stationery to correspond with the image of your company. Business cards should be easy to read – do not overdo with pictures and a lot of text. Listing a few key benefits on quality paper can be very effective.

Brochures and Fliers – Many companies will use brochures and fliers as sales tools. This can be very cost-effective since you can make your best sales pitch with all the benefits you offer. Use the same typestyle, color, and logo on your brochures and fliers.

Signs – The sign for your business is critical. Again, use the same typestyle, color, and logo. The most common mistake with signs is when they are too small to read at any distance. Use as large of print as possible. You may have to forego your logo if you don't have room. If a customer cannot see your sign and read it, you have wasted your money. Before you invest in a sign, check into city and state zoning requirements to find if there are any sign restrictions.

Communication – When talking with your customers, always be positive and upbeat or reasonable, *no matter what*. Customers like to do business with people who sound successful and optimistic.

The key word for image/packaging is: *consistency*. This relates to all issues we've just identified.

If you choose red for your company color, use red for your logo, in your sign and on your brochures. Don't use one color for one thing, and then switch to another color for another thing. If you use a certain typestyle for your business cards, use the same typestyle on your sign. Keep the same theme for every way your customer sees your business.

You and your business should have and maintain a first-class image in this competitive marketplace if you wish to succeed. A poor image can kill a company quicker than anything. If you hope to get your business off the ground, enter the marketplace with your best foot forward.

Worksheets to help you plan your packaging and promotion strategies are on the following pages.

Two important steps during this planning process are to *get feedback* and to *listen and be objective.* Objective people include your business counselor, prospective customers, even competitors. Understand why they are critical and have them explain why they like or don't like what you have planned.

Worksheet—Image/Packaging

1. What will your carton or wrapping look like?

a) How much will it cost to produce?

b) Who will produce it? Where will you buy it?

2. Where is your office/store located? What does it look like?

a) Why did you choose this location?

b) What nearby businesses will help attract customers?

c) What are the prospects of business growth in the area?

3. **What does your office/store layout look like? Sketch a diagram of floor space indicating equipment, furniture and fixtures. If the space below is not large enough, use a separate piece of paper.**

4. Will you rent or buy this space, and how much will it cost?

a) ___ Will operate from home.

> If you will operate your business from your home, answer the questions in this section about costs, preparation, and location. Also – what space are you taking from your family or lifestyle? How will this work for you?

b) ___ Rent	Monthly rent payment	$
Lease period_____months:	Insurance	$
	Utilities	$
c) ___ Buy	Monthly mortgage payment	$
Mortgage term____years	Real estate taxes	$
Interest rate_____% Purchase price$_____	Other costs (describe)	$
Down payment$_____	Other costs (describe)	$

5. What type of remodeling is required, and at what cost?

Heating	$	Flooring	$
Air conditioning	$	Roofing	$
Electrical	$	Bathrooms	$
Fixtures	$	Decorating	$
Exhaust	$	Permits	$
Plumbing	$		$
	$		$
Total this column	$	Total this column	$
		Subtotal	$
Add contingency amount as a percent of subtotal		%	$
		Grand total	$

Get written bids from contractors, plumbers, and others to include in your business plan.

6. How long will it take to prepare your business site?

7. How will you provide handicap access?

8. Does your product style fit your desired image? Why or why not?

9. What is the name of your business?

a) Check with your state to determine if you must register your business name. If so, what process should you follow, and how much will it cost?

1

2

3

b) If you have a slogan or subtitle, what is it?

10. Will you have a logo? If so what will it look like?

a) How much will it cost to produce?

b) Who will produce it?

CORE FOUR® Business Planning Course

11. Will you have a company color? If so, what color and why?

12. What typestyle will you use? What does it look like?

13. What will your business cards and stationery look like?

a) How much will it cost to produce?

b) Who will produce it?

14. Will you use brochures for customers? What will they promote? If so, what will they look like? Include samples in your business plan.

a) How much will they cost to produce?

b) Who will produce them?

15. Will you need a sign for your business? If so, what will it look like?

How big will it be?

a) How much will it cost to produce?

b) Who will produce it?

c) How much will it cost to install?

d) What city, county or other zoning regulations apply? If permits or fees are required to put up your sign, how much will they cost?

16. What will YOU look like? How will you dress? How will your employees dress?

a) If you have uniforms, how many will you need and how much will they cost?

b) Where will you get uniforms?

CREATE A PROMOTIONAL PLAN

WHY DO CUSTOMERS BUY?
WHAT'S IN IT FOR THEM?

People buy for *benefits* – not *features*. People will not buy products or services if they are not aware of them, nor will they buy products or services if they do not understand them or care about them.

It is your job to make consumers aware of your products and services. You must make your customers understand why your products or services are better than those of competitors, and what benefits customers are buying. When creating your promotional plan, use benefit statements that your customers will understand.

So far you have defined your features and benefits and positioned your business in the marketplace. Now you can figure out how to make your customers aware of your uniqueness. Use your position in the marketplace to build customer awareness and preference for buying from you.

HOW DO YOU USE BENEFITS TO MOTIVATE CUSTOMERS?

Use benefits to appeal to your customers in two ways: with fear and self-interest. Does this sound unappealing? Think of every ad or commercial you have ever read or seen. They appeal to you in two ways: with fear and self-interest.

If you use fear to motivate a customer, be careful: everyone has insecurities and doubts. Tell people how *not* buying your product will affect them, or show them what they will be missing if they do not purchase your product. Use *rational* reasons. Do not push or intimidate your customer in order to get the sale. Use believable reasons, or you will lose your credibility and hurt your image and business.

To appeal to self-interests, show your customers how you are filling their needs or wants. When appealing to your customers' self-interest, you can use *emotional or rational* reasons depending on what you sell. When you are selling a product that fills a *need*, you will be more effective with your message if you use *rational* reasons. If you are filling a *want*, use *emotional* reasons to motivate your customers.

"Helloooooo? Is anybody home?"

A business with no sign is a sign of no business!

The chart on the following page shows you how to use your benefits and when to use each type of reasoning.

Motivation Chart

SAMPLE BENEFITS	You Are Filling A Need (Food, Shelter, Transportation...)	You Are Filling A Want (Comfort, Gender Appeal, Status...)
Rational reasons:		
Durability	√	
Economy	√	
Handiness	√	
Efficiency	√	
Dependability	√	
Emotional reasons:		
Memories		√
Cleanliness		√
Pleasure		√
Love		√
Loyalty		√
Ambition		√

When using *rational* reasons to motivate your customers, facts and customer testimonials will make your products or services more credible. You also can use guarantees and test results to help customers understand the benefits of your products or services.

When using *emotional* reasons to appeal to your customers, the stronger the appeal, the more likely your customers will buy your products or services. Some customers need excuses to buy, so give them what they want. Haven't you ever let your heart dictate to your head when making a purchase?

WHAT ARE THE THREE BASIC OBJECTIVES WHEN PROMOTING YOUR PRODUCT?

1. Get the customer's attention.
2. Convey a simple message stating the benefits to the customer.
3. Ask for action – what do you want your customer to do after seeing your message?

If customers are not aware of your products or services, they will not buy them. How do you make your customers aware of your business? Promote it!

The answer is simple, but doing it can be difficult. Your customers are bombarded daily with more than 500 advertising messages. When you drive to work, you hear many messages on the radio and see billboards or signs everywhere. When you get home, you may read a newspaper or magazine and see even more messages. Have you ever counted the number of commercials you see in an hour of television? You may be surprised at how many advertising messages are thrown at you daily. The question then becomes – why do some messages stick and others do not?

Getting the customer's attention is the toughest step. Your packaging can help get the customer's attention, but you need to do more. Always put your customer in the message. Use words like: You, Your, or Yourself. Use questions to challenge the customer. Start your headlines with words like: Who, What, When, Where, Why, How, or Which. Consider using pictures or demonstrations to get your customer's attention.

Next, create a simple message using benefit

statements that the customer can relate to and understand. A common mistake is to cram too much information at the consumer. Use one of the following *themes* for your messages:

1. Inform of the benefits of your product or service.
2. Change the image of your product, service, or business.
3. Teach something new about your product, service, or business.
4. Remind of past satisfaction with your product or service.

Finally, tell the customer what to do after seeing your message:

1. Buy your product or service.
2. Try your product or service on a trial offer.
3. Come to see your business.
4. Call for a brochure.
5. Call for more information.

Always tell the customer how to reach you. Include your business name, address, city, state, telephone number, email address, and/or web address.

HOW MUCH SHOULD YOU SPEND ON PROMOTION?

There is no standard amount. Generally, businesses spend between 2% to 7% of their *operating budget* on promotion. The key is to spend cash efficiently and effectively. To make the most of your investment, get the *right* message to the *right* person at the *right* time. This is where target marketing comes in – use your customer profile information to help target your message.

You have many options for promoting your product or service. The lists on the following pages show these options, the positives and negatives, and some alternative low-cost ideas. The key is to get your message to only the people who need to hear it.

Another common mistake is talking to a larger market than necessary. Let's say you restore antique cars. Does it make sense to advertise on television when only a very small group of viewers would be interested in your service? When more people get your message than need to, you have spent your money unwisely. You could spend your money more effectively by advertising in automobile magazines that focus on antique and collector cars.

Let's say you install lawn-sprinkler systems. Does it make sense to advertise on television in the winter months? People do not care about their lawns in the winter months. Using the antique car restoration business, would it make more sense to advertise on television during soap operas or car clinic shows? Think about when cereal or toy commercials are on television – usually every Saturday morning when kids are watching cartoons. Did you ever wonder why?

The amount of advertising dollars you should spend will depend on the level of your aggressiveness and your competition's method. It also will depend on the seasonality of your business. Advertising is costly, and it is a commitment your business must make. Spend your money wisely.

HOW SHOULD YOU ADVERTISE?

Repetition is key. Customers need to see or hear your message *at least 6 times* to remember it. Pick one medium and do a thorough job before trying another form. For example, if you choose to promote your product in the newspaper, run your message 6 times and evaluate the results before you decide to switch to another medium, such as radio.

Lastly, track the responses from each of your promotional efforts. Ask your customers how they heard about your business or product. This allows you to know what promotion technique is working for you.

PROMOTIONAL OPTIONS

Paid Advertising
    One-on-One Selling
Radio
    Presentation materials
Television/Cable
    Personal letters
Newspapers - Display Ads
    Customized proposals
Newspapers - Classified Ads

Magazines
Shoppers
    Sales Promotions
Yellow Pages
    Discounts
Special directories
    Loss leaders
Trade/Industry directories
    Coupons
Indoor/Outdoor billboards
    Contests

Direct Mail
    Specialty Advertising
Letters
    Matchbooks, key chains,
Newsletters
    and other novelties
Sales or product/service
    Calendars
announcements
    Date books
Customers
    Magnetic business cards
Postcards
Brochures
    Facilities
Coupons
    Site location and shared
    advertising

    Signs
Public Relations
    Window displays
News releases
    Point of purchase displays
Articles in magazines, journals
    Fixture and layout of store
Open Houses
    Lighting
Speaking engagements
Interview shows
    Other Types of Promotion
Sponsorship of community events
    Magnetic car signs

Seminars/Workshops
    Posters
Club memberships
    Blimps and balloons
Public Service Announcements
    Free samples
Trade Shows
    Handouts

    Sandwich boards
Telemarketing
    Signs on buses and taxis
Surveys
    Word of mouth
Direct sales
    Web site

TYPES OF PAID ADVERTISING

TYPE	POSITIVE	NEGATIVE
Television	High visibility and impact Can demonstrate your product	High cost Harder to target
Radio	Better targeting	Cost Message is in background
Magazine	Better targeting High quality-better image Customer is actively seeking	Less impact Builds awareness more slowly
Newspaper (Placement in appropriate section)	Credible and acceptable Customer is seeking	Low impact
Yellow Pages	Customer is actively seeking	Costly Printed only once a year
Public Relations	Free	Hard to get
Direct Mail	Better targeting	Low response: 1% - 2%
Trade Shows	Highly qualified sales lists	Costly, timely
Shoppers (papers)	Appeals to price consciousness Everybody receives Less expensive than other papers	Rarely read throughout Low quality
Outdoor/Transit	Size Impact Target by location Effective for simple messages	Inflexible Can be costly Message can physically deteriorate
Specialty Items	Usefulness of product ensures longevity of message Better targeting	Limited space for message Difficult to evaluate success of this type of promotion
Web Site	Searched by someone who wants what you sell	Commitment to maintain and keep interesting and current Can be expensive and time-consuming.

LOW COST MARKETING IDEAS

The intent of promotion is to *increase your sales* by making the public aware of your products or services. Every $1 spent on promotion should produce additional dollars in sales – at least $1 to cover the cost of the promotion, *and additional dollars for overhead and profit*. If you do not expect to achieve additional sales, then *do not* spend the money on promotion.

The best and cheapest way to advertise is by "word of mouth." Customer recommendations and referrals can sway a consumer's buying decision for or against you. *Treat everyone you meet as a potential customer.*

Other than "word of mouth" advertising, making the public aware of your business can be an expensive proposition. Here are some low-cost marketing ideas that should help promote your business. As you read these ideas, think of how you could adapt them to your own situation.

1. Put your business card on any bulletin board you see.

2. Place an ad in your church bulletin. Perhaps offer your service/product in exchange for free advertising.

3. Send inquiring wholesale customers a sample of your product and price list instead of creating an expensive catalog or brochure. They will be able to see the quality of your product and will never forget the gift.

4. Watch your newspaper for new business listings. Send the owners congratulatory letters and tell them about your product/service. Follow up with a visit or phone call.

5. Contact Senior Citizen Groups (if they are part of your target customer population) to inform them of your services. When a senior citizen needs a particular service, they could be referred to you as opposed to someone else.

6. Join the Chamber of Commerce or other networking groups and attend all their functions. This is another inexpensive way to make additional business contacts.

7. Advertise on restaurant menus and placemats– this is usually inexpensive, and you can target your customers more directly.

8. Call the phone company regarding the cost of Yellow Page advertising. *If you have a business line,* most Yellow Page directories should include your phone number in one of the Yellow Page categories *free of charge – but sometimes you need to ask!*

9. Write informational or how-to articles about your product/service and submit them to the newspaper. The newspaper is more apt to print stories that will benefit its readers. In addition, you will sound like an expert and get some free advertising in the process.

10. Send a press release to the newspaper in your area at least quarterly – to announce new hires, business milestones, or professional achievements. There is no guarantee they will be printed, but to not do it is a guarantee that it won't be printed!

11. See the Yellow Pages for associations, clubs, fraternities, or organizations. Contact these groups to see if they produce newsletters. If so, advertise in their newsletters. It should be less expensive than advertising in the newspaper and may target your customers more specifically.

12. Send "Hi, Neighbor" letters to people in your neighborhood telling them who you are and what you do.

13. Offer to teach at schools or association meetings. Offer businesses mini-seminars or one-time sessions on topics related to your business.

14. Enclose your business cards with the personal bills you pay, i.e., dry cleaners, lawn service, plumbers, etc. Let them know who is spending money with them.

15. Leave freebies (pens, key chains, pencils, calendars, etc.) with customers as a "thank you" for the business or opportunity to bid for the business. *Use common sense with this idea* – it's easy to go overboard with specialty advertising.

16. Contact local, state, and federal governments and ask to be put on their bidder lists.

17. Contact radio and television stations and offer to barter your product or services for free advertising.

18. Donate playing cards (with your business name on the backs of the cards) to senior citizen centers if seniors are your targeted customers.

19. Use magnetic car signs *with care*. If you have a presentable car and good, courteous driving skills, your name and business will be seen everywhere you go. Take the sign off if you are goofing off.

20. Wear a nametag (shirt, hat, or jacket) with both your name and business name on it whenever you are in public (except when you are goofing off). Often people forget your name and are too embarrassed to ask you again. This lets them off the hook. Sometimes the nametag will even stimulate a conversation and let you inform another potential customer of your business. Caution: when you are dressed for "work," always look and behave professionally. With uniforms, make a rule that your employees wear them in the workplace only, and that they keep them clean and in good repair.

21. Create a referral list of satisfied customers and distribute it with your other promotional material to all potential customers. Be sure you have *permission* to use their names for referral.

22. Hold a contest offering a free prize. This is a great way to get additional leads or names for your mailing list. If the customer must buy something in order to enter the contest, this also should increase sales. *Follow state laws when holding a contest or raffle.*

23. Consider using a bulk mailing service if you are planning a mass mailing. These services can combine your mail with theirs and offer you a lower postage rate than you could get on your own.

24. Produce a wall calendar that also serves as a catalog (with order form) for your customers. This is a clever way to have your name in front of the customer all year!

25. Display your products or sales brochures about your products (with your name and how you can be reached) in other business locations. The reverse can work for you as well. For example, if you sell plants, offer to display your plants in someone else's business with a sign telling people where the plants came from.

26. Use indoor advertising (signs mounted on the doors of rest room stalls) in public places. This is not as expensive as you think when you consider your name will be shown to hundreds of people who will have the time to read your message.

27. Consider using the classified section of the newspaper to promote your product/services. It is less expensive than a display advertisement, and the classified section is a well-read section of the newspaper.

28. Consider having stick-on labels made with your company's name, address, and phone number. Place these labels on all of your products. This will remind your customers of where they got your products.

29. Consider having the Boy Scouts or another organization hand out samples or flyers to customers in targeted neighborhoods.

30. Consider asking a cleaning service to leave your brochure/business cards at their customers' homes.

31. Talk with other businesses that might want to share advertising expenses. Consider using both company names on TV or radio advertisements. TV and radio ads are expensive, and this is a way to cut these cost in half.

32. Consider speaking on your public radio station or doing an informational session on your community television station. There is usually no cost for these opportunities.

33. Consider speaking at a public event where you can describe your services or be an expert to answer questions for the audience.

34. Above all else, *ensure high customer satisfaction*. A happy customer will tell three others about your company – while a dissatisfied customer will tell 20 others not to use your company.

Make the most of your advertising dollars. It is easy to spend a lot of money on traditional forms of marketing and not receive any payback. Make the most of your marketing dollars by spending them on methods that *directly target* your customers.

Remember:

> ***Every dollar spent on promotion must produce additional dollars of sales.***

E-COMMERCE AND YOUR WEBSITE

"Build it and they will come."

Yes, it's a whisper from beyond in a famous movie about baseball. It should <u>not</u> be the philosophy behind your website.

The use of a website should be considered when planning your market. Considerations relating to a website should be discussed in each topic of your marketing plan. For instance, if you are going to sell handmade birdhouses over the Internet, will you be prepared if a pet store e-mails you with an order for twelve dozen? You will be if you go through your distribution process. Defining your customer profile and conducting research surveys will help you understand the likes and dislikes of people who buy birdhouses. This in turn will help you identify where on the Internet to market your site and what key words to use in order for search engines to pick them up. Pricing and competition are two more examples of Internet research needed before you launch your website.

Purpose of Your Website

Considerations of the type of product or service you offer become very important in e-commerce. It would be hard for a chiropractor to make adjustments to your knee injury online, but you could make an appointment with your chiropractor. What would your customers use your website to gain? Information? Ideas? Products? Appointments? Help?

Keep in mind that there are different uses of websites for different products or distribution methods. Take a look at the following websites:

www.jello.com   www.prego.com
www.mayo.com   www.ragu.com

What do you notice about these sites?
They are used for consumer information. These brand name product sites give you information and ideas, prompting you to buy, leaving the sales to the wholesalers and retailers in their distribution process.

Cost Analysis

Consider cost in planning your website. Most home-based or small retailers don't understand the startup cost of building and maintaining a website, nor do they consider the time involved daily in checking for orders, answering questions or e-mails, and making shipping and payment arrangements.

Would it be possible to spend so much time on the Internet with your vendors and doing your bookkeeping that you have no time for your retail store customers? Will Internet sales allow for you to hire, at least part-time, someone to cover your retail store hours? Will your business benefit from having a website?

Marketing Your Website

Like the need for a market plan and advertising plan for your business, your website might be enhanced and grow with a marketing plan and an advertising plan as well. Once launched, how will customers find your site? Do you need to list your website on your business card and brochures? In your newspaper ads? Do you need to consider buying banners on other favorite sites your customers use? Have you considered links to and from other websites?

The information given here is by no means a comprehensive plan to building your website. If you consider using a website, thoroughly research the considerations presented here.

Worksheet—Promotional Plan

1. What is your promotional message?

2. What forms of promotion will you use? Why?

Type	Why

3. What will you ask your customers to do?

Example—Promotional Plan

ACTION	WHO IS RESPONSIBLE	BY WHEN	COST
Get into Yellow Pages	Me	June 1	$240.00
Call paper for press release	Me	June 1	$0.00
Get business cards printed	Me	June 15	$50.00
Get ad in newspaper	Partner	July 1	$35.00

Create Your Promotional Plan

Promotional Plan			
Action	Who is Responsible	By When	Cost

PRICING YOUR PRODUCTS OR SERVICES

WHAT SHOULD YOU CONSIDER WHEN PRICING YOUR PRODUCTS OR SERVICES?

Pricing is an art and a science. The art is market strategy. The science is cash flow, which will be discussed during the Cash Flow Planning segment of this course.

This section on pricing deals with market strategy, the art of recognizing that price is not a personal issue, that a lower price is not always better, and that the marketplace will help you determine the highest price the market can bear.

Five market strategies concerning pricing are discussed below:

1. *A lower price is not always better.* Customers often associate price with quality. Have you ever found yourself buying a higher priced product because you assumed it was better? Most people, if they are honest, will answer *yes* to this question. Depending on the quality of your product, the desired image of your company, and the other services you offer, sell the value of your business rather than the price of your product.

2. *Use your strengths as your competitive advantage* to sway customers to buy from you instead of someone else. You operate in a competitive market. Comparison shopping does exist. Price is not the only criteria evaluated by customers. You evaluated your competition on a number of other considerations including, but not limited to:

   Quality
   Availability
   Expertise
   Service after the sale
   Image
   Convenience

   Remember when you compared yourself to the competition? Educate your customers about your strengths. Again, sell the *value* of your business rather than the price of your product.

3. *Customers, depending on who they are and what you sell, may have a limited ability to pay* for your products or services. Generally, people will price-shop for things they need. When people are filling their wants, they are willing to pay for value. If you have a truly wonderful product or service, but your customers cannot afford it, you will have a difficult time selling regardless of the benefits your business offers.

4. *Price can be used to control the supply and demand of your products and services.* If you find your business unable to keep up with customer orders, your image or reputation could suffer because you are not responding fast enough to meet your customers' wants or needs. Your solution could be raising prices. As price increases, demand will decrease.

5. *Price testing is critical.* When offering new products or services, price them differently in different segments of the marketplace and measure the impact on sales. Keep adjusting your price until your customer orders are at a level you can handle.

The following chart depicts typical pricing formulas and outlines all the costs you should consider.

BASIC PRICING FORMULA

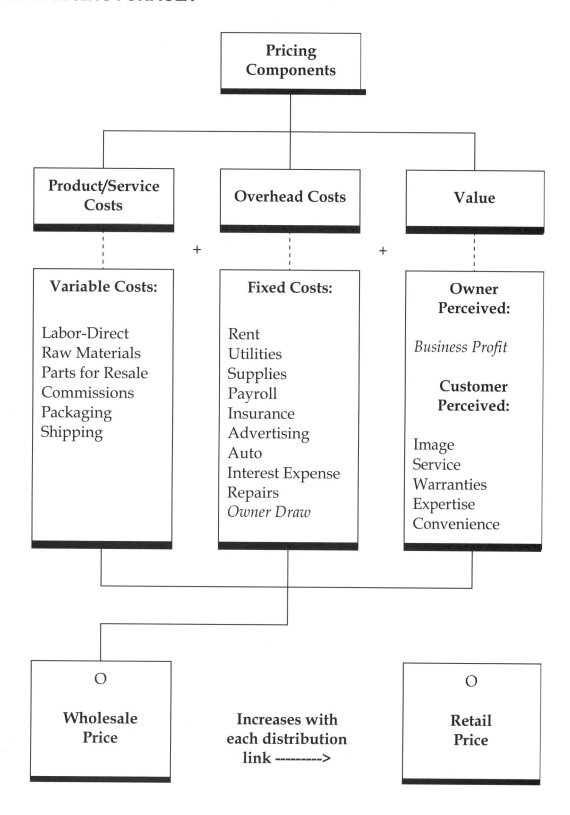

Pricing Components

Product/Service Costs + **Overhead Costs** + **Value**

Variable Costs:

Labor-Direct
Raw Materials
Parts for Resale
Commissions
Packaging
Shipping

Fixed Costs:

Rent
Utilities
Supplies
Payroll
Insurance
Advertising
Auto
Interest Expense
Repairs
Owner Draw

Owner Perceived:

Business Profit

Customer Perceived:

Image
Service
Warranties
Expertise
Convenience

O
Wholesale Price

Increases with each distribution link --------->

O
Retail Price

WHAT ARE VARIABLE COSTS?

Variable costs are directly tied to the sale of your product. These costs include things such as the direct labor to make your product, parts, raw materials, and packaging. If you did not sell or make your product, you would have no variable costs.

WHAT ARE FIXED COSTS?

Fixed costs are *committed* costs. If you commit to having a business, you will commit to these costs *whether or not you sell* your product. These costs include rent, utilities, office supplies, advertising, and travel. Sometimes these costs are referred to as the *costs of doing business*. They also include what you have identified as your need for take-home pay, *owner draw*. Your owner draw must be covered or it is not worth your time and effort to operate your business – and you won't have enough money to take care of your personal needs.

WHAT ARE VALUE COSTS?

There are two types of value costs, yours and your customers'. Yours is the value you should receive from operating your business – you deserve to profit from operating your business. The second is the value your customers perceive in doing business with your company. Remember, you may charge an additional price for added value such as convenience, warranties, location, expertise, quality, and other services.

Consider all the pricing components when setting your price. If you do not, your business will simply lose money. Again, the basic definition of marketing is "Meeting a customer need or want at a profit." You have already gathered some of your costs, but you will pull them all together when you start your business financial planning.

The worksheet on the following page will help you identify your costs.

Worksheet—Pricing: Identify Your Cost Types

Check (√) the boxes for the types of costs you will have for each category – actual dollars are not necessary at this time.

	VARIABLE COSTS		FIXED COSTS		VALUE COSTS
	Labor-Direct		Rent		Business Profit
	Raw Materials		Utilities		Product Selection
	Parts		Office Supplies		Quality
	Commission		Payroll		Availability
	Packaging		Insurance		Warranties
	Shipping		Advertising		Expertise
	Inventory		Auto		Service After the Sale
	Waste Disposal		Loan/Interest		Reputation
	Purchases for resale		Repairs		Image/Appearance
			Furniture/Fixtures		Location
			Equipment		Customization
			Remodeling Costs		Reliability
			Legal/Accounting		Credit Policy
			Licenses/Permits		Management
			Maintenance		Customer Service
			Dues/Subscriptions		
			Trash Removal		
			Entertainment		
			Bank Charges		
			Owner Draw		

DIRECT SELLING: THE SALES PRESENTATION

WHO WILL YOU BE SELLING TO?

Many businesses do not have to go door-to-door to sell their products or services, but *everyone has to sell their business, products, and services to someone*. You may have to sell your business to any or all of the following people:

- Customers
- Bankers/Lenders/Investors
- Vendors/Suppliers
- Consignment Stores
- Family/Friends
- Yourself!

Each person has different needs or wants, and you should understand them. You already know you have to sell to customers, but what if you need money to start your business? You will need to talk with a banker, lender, or investor and sell the idea of lending you the money. If you need raw materials or supplies, you will work with your vendors or suppliers and sell them on the idea of establishing an account with credit. If you are working with a consignment store, you will sell the owner on using valuable floor space to display your products. You will even find yourself selling your business to family and friends to gain their support.

Most importantly, *sell to yourself*! By developing a comprehensive business plan, you will build your own confidence about the achievability of your success and the value of what your business offers. When you are confident, people have confidence in you.

This list does not cover everyone, but you get the idea that the process of selling your business begins *before* you even open your door.

HOW DO YOU FEEL ABOUT SELLING YOUR PRODUCTS OR SERVICES?

Most people hate the thought of selling. Why? Perhaps because you remember the hard tactics someone may have used on you while you squirmed uncomfortably? You're shy? You don't like talking to people? You don't want to make people do something they might not want to do? You tried selling and were not successful?

The most important thing to remember is that *selling is not about you*. It is about your customer. Selling, when done right, is a strategy for communicating *with*, not to, another person. The objective of the strategy is to help your customer make an informed choice about buying your products or services. The ideal outcome is a sale. The second ideal outcome is that both you and your customer feel good about the exchange.

Consider yourself a consultant, not a salesperson. Your objective is to help the customer make an informed choice. This keeps the focus on the customer, *where it belongs*. Though you may not personally care about the needs or wants of your customers, you must understand them. If you do not, you will have a tough time selling anything to anyone.

If you can focus on customer needs, you will show them that you care about them and not about making the sale. Once your customers *trust* and *believe* you have their best interests at heart, you will have a better chance for success.

For the customer to believe in you, you must be honest, and you must *listen* to what they want, need, or have to say.
If your product or service cannot meet your customer's need, say so. If you can, recommend a solution or alternative, even if it's a competitor. The customer will appreciate your willingness to help them find what they need. "Well, he was really fair and above board," or, "she really knew what she was talking about, and I'm glad she spent the time with me." How many times have you left a communication with a salesperson and thought this to yourself? Did you feel that you just worked with a true *professional?* That's how you want your customer to feel.

People may not remember what you said.
People may not remember what you did.
People will always remember how you made them feel.

Think about your own experiences when you have dealt with people trying to sell you things. What did you like – what didn't you like? Even though honesty may cost you this sale, it will have a payback. This customer may not buy from you, but they may tell others how honest you were and may tell them to give you a call.

CORE FOUR® Business Planning Course

Remember: word-of-mouth advertising is not only the cheapest; it's the most influential.

Listening is an art. Don't you feel good when you believe someone really understands what you want or need? And doesn't it frustrate you when they don't?

By taking the focus off selling and putting the focus *on the customer*, you no longer are selling. Instead, you are helping them – this will make the selling process a lot easier.

An example sales presentation is on the following pages.

Review this presentation and complete the worksheets following the presentation.

Example—Sales Presentation

Step 1: Introduce yourself and your company, products or services.

When meeting people you do not know, always introduce yourself and your company.

> **Example A:** You are selling your polar-fleece mittens at a bazaar when a woman comes up to your table. Greet that customer and say something like, "Hi, I am Suzy Jacobs with Grizzly-Fleece Wear."

> **Example B:** You are meeting with a lender to ask for startup financing for your business. Introduce yourself by saying, "Hi, I am Suzy Jacobs, President of Grizzly-Fleece Wear. My business manufactures outdoor winter accessories."

> *Smile. It will make you both feel better. The customer may be just as uncomfortable as you.*

Step 2: Build rapport.

Before you go any further, stop and take a moment to build rapport with this person. Try to break the ice by asking the person something about their business or job. Stay away from asking anything personal, since many people may be offended by personal questions. Be prepared to ask a couple of open-ended questions (open-ended questions require more than a Yes or No response), then ask additional questions based on the response you get. Make *conversation*.

There are three reasons for breaking the ice. First, it will let the person know you are interested in them. Second, it gives you time to compose yourself and not get nervous. Third, it gives you a chance to get to know the person. You want the customer to like and trust you because "People don't buy things – they buy things from people." Moreover, they like to buy things from people they like.

> **Example A:** You could ask the woman where she is from. Then ask her additional questions about the climate there or something else about her home city. A bazaar is a casual environment, but you are a business owner. The conversation may be slightly more social than as in example B.

> **Example B:** You could ask the lender, "How long have you been with this bank?" You could follow up with "How long have you been making commercial loans?"

Step 3: State your objective.

Tell the person why you are there. Let the person know from the beginning whether you are trying to sell something, informing them about your product or service, or asking for help getting financing.

> **Example A:** Because you are at a bazaar, the customer knows your objective so you could skip this step. In a retail environment, the customer is shopping. They know why they are there, which might be to buy something from you.

> **Example B:** With the lender, you could say you are seeking help to get startup financing. Currently you are making sample products out of your home and want to move to an industrial site and formalize your business. (Note that you don't ask the lender for a loan or for money, but for the lender's help to get a loan).

Step 4: Ask your customer about his/her needs.

Listen carefully and ask for additional information if you do not understand. This step can make or break your presentation.

> **Example A:** Ask if the customer is looking for something in particular. The customer says, "I am looking for a warm pair of mittens that will last a long time."

Example B: If you are talking to a lender, ask what information the lender uses to make a favorable decision about a loan. The lender may ask for information about your collateral, credit worthiness, and ability to repay the loan. The lender will also want a copy of your business plan and cash flow projections. Remember that when you are selling your ideas or concepts, it is important for the other *person to believe in you and to want to help you.*

Step 5: State your product or service features and benefits.

Describe features and benefits that will fill the needs the customer has stated. *Do not* try to fill needs that have not been expressed; handle each need one at a time.

Example A: When talking to your customer, you could explain that because of the grizzly-fleece lining in your mittens, hands will stay warm even in 30-degree below-zero weather. You could explain that because of the double stitching, the mittens are designed to last at least five years under normal use.

Example B: When responding to a lender, be prepared to talk in *lender terms* about credit and collateral. Know what you have to pledge, and be honest about your credit history. If there are any gray areas, including collateral that may not be greater than the loan value, or a credit history that is not perfect, you may sway a favorable decision by selling the benefits of your business knowledge and commitment. The best way to do this is to emphasize your cash flow projections and how they show your ability to repay the loan. The benefit to the lender is that you demonstrate that have done your homework, have detailed knowledge about your business, and have planned for all your future sales and expenses.

Step 6: Summarize your benefits.

When you are done stating your features and benefits, summarize *only the benefits the customer wants.*

Example A: When talking to the customer about your mittens, you could say something like, "So, as you can see, not only are these mittens warm, they will last you a long time."

Example B: When summarizing for the loan officer, you would say something like, "In response to your needs, you can see that I plan to operate a successful business to repay this loan, and I am willing to pledge my collateral to assure you of my commitment to repay this loan. You can see that I always keep my promises, and how I have planned to repay your loan."

Step 7: Ask for the business.

Many people never ask for the business and lose a lot of sales. After summarizing your benefits, *ask for the business.* Then you *must not* say another word. There is a saying, "He who speaks next, loses." Do not start talking or giving more information. Assume the customer will answer yes, even if you are not sure. After all, you just addressed all of the customer's needs. Let the customer answer Yes or No or ask additional questions. Listen. Clarify and answer all the customers' questions. *Ask* for the business again or ask when you can meet again.

Example A: After summarizing the benefits for your customer, you would ask, "Can I wrap these up for you?"

Example B: When talking with the loan officer, simply state you would like a loan for 'X' dollars. Chances are the loan officer will need to review your business plan and cash flows. Ask for a follow-up appointment. At that appointment, let the loan officer tell you specifically what more you need to provide. Then ask, "If I provide all the additional information, will I then get the loan?"

Step 8: Thank your customers for their business or their time.

This is a step that is often overlooked. *Always* thank all of your customers for their business, or for spending the time to discuss your products or services, *whether or not they buy from you.* Common courtesy never goes out of style. Everyone appreciates a thank you. If you do not thank the customer, the customer may think you really do not care, and next time, the customer may not be so willing to do business with you. "Thanks for stopping by," at the bazaar, or "Thanks for taking the time to meet with me," to the banker are appropriate no matter what the outcome.

HOW CAN YOU BE MORE SUCCESSFUL AT SELLING?

You do not have to care personally about the customer's need. If you do, however, the customer will sense it. As long as you focus on the customer's need or want, you should be more successful.

Above all else, be honest. Your reputation is at stake. It is your most valuable asset.

Whenever possible, use customer testimonials or customer references to gain credibility. This is almost as good as a personal recommendation. Always get the customers' permission before using their names. This can take time, but the time to build a satisfied customer reference list will be well worth it.

When creating your advertising literature, use all of the benefit statements you have developed. Good promotional literature can help you in more than one way. It will tell your message when you are not with the customer. It will help you when you are with a customer. It can be used as a guide if you tend to get nervous and forget to state an important point.

ALWAYS EXUDE SUCCESS

This means showing the customer that you are positive and successful. People like to do business with people who are positive, confident, and cheerful. If you are having a bad day, *never* let it show. Keep smiling – *no matter what*.

BE PERSISTENT

Keep going. Keep trying. Don't feel badly about not getting the sale – just move on. Anyone who is successful will tell you that they never gave up.

THE TRUTH: PERSISTENCY PAYS OFF

80% - of all sales are made after the fifth call

48% - of all salespeople make one call and quit

25% - of all salespeople call twice and quit

10% - of all salespeople keep calling

80% - of all sales are made by only 10% of all salespeople

Worksheet—Creating Your Sales Presentation

When creating your sales presentation, follow this order for two reasons: First, it is more effective with the customer, and second, the more you practice and use a routine, the better you can present yourself. Regardless of whom you are selling to, all steps still apply.

1. What are some open-ended questions you can ask to build rapport?

2. What are some benefit statements you will use for the following people?

Customers	
Lenders	
Vendors/Suppliers	
Family	

3. What facts or data will help you with your sales presentation? Do you have a satisfied customer referral list?

BUILD YOUR MARKETING PLAN

HOW DO YOU BUILD YOUR MARKETING PLAN?

By now, you have all the answers! You've done the planning, and now can write your plan! You can verify if you have all the answers by answering the questions in the market planning section of the business plan outline on pages 23-SP – 26-SP in this book. If there is a question in the outline that you do not know the answer to, it's time to do more homework!

Your marketing plan will be the major and most important section of your business plan. It will be the destination on your road map. It presents your opportunities for success, and your strategies for building a successful business.

WHAT DO YOU DO NOW THAT YOUR MARKETING PLAN IS DONE?

Congratulations! You have done a lot of work and now can share your Marketing Plan with others. After all, when you get a new car, you probably like to show it off because you are proud of it and want others to see it. You should be proud of your marketing plan – so show it off! Once you have created your marketing plan, you are ready to use it as a guide.

You probably think you are done, and you are – well, almost. Review your marketing plan every three to six months to see how you are doing. *It is a waste of your time and money to plan if you do not evaluate the results of your plan.* Review your plan for the following:

1. Did your plan deliver the desired results?
2. What was the effect of your actions?
3. Did you stay within your budget?
4. How did your competition respond?
5. Do you need to make any changes?

CASH FLOW PLANNING

CONTENTS

FIGURE IT OUT

Let's say you allow yourself $10 per day from your household budget (your cookie jar), Monday through Friday, for spending money. You use this cash to buy your lunch, park your car, whatever. For entertainment, you use it to rent a video, go bowling, go to a movie, or have dinner with a friend. During the week, you will receive $50 and you will spend $50. Each morning you take $10 from your cookie jar.

Here's your plan:

Monday morning start with $10
   Park in ramp – $3
   Buy a doughnut and coffee – $2
   Get soup from the deli and a bottle of soda for lunch – $5
   Total cash out = $10

Tuesday morning get $10
   Park in ramp – $3
   Lunch with a friend – $7
   Total cash out = $10

Wednesday morning get $10
   Park in ramp – $3
   Lunch and a soda - $5
   Total cash out = $8

Thursday morning get $10
   Park in ramp – $3
   Lunch with mom – $8
   Total cash out = $11

Friday morning get $10
   Park in ramp – $3
   Leave early, go to movie – $8
   Total cash out $11

Weekly totals:
   Cash in = $50
   Cash out = $50

Will your plan work? Use the worksheet below to figure it out. The first two days have been completed. No matter what the numbers end up to be, do the math through Friday.

Your ending cash is how much cash you have "in your pocket." When you take your $10 from the cookie jar, you will add it to the cash "in your pocket."

	Mon	Tue	Wed	Thur	Fri
Cash on hand (in your pocket)	0	0	0	2	1
Plus cash in (from cookie jar)	10	10	10	10	10
Minus cash out	-10	-10	-8	-11	-11
= Ending cash (in your pocket)	0	0	2	1	0

After you complete the plan, what questions do you have?

Congratulations! You just finished a cash flow projection!

The results of your cash flow plan will help you understand whether or not your business idea is:

feasible – can you get it to be a business?

and

viable – can it stay a business?

Was your personal plan in the previous exercise feasible? Could you establish a weekly cash flow plan with the assumptions that were made? Would your personal plan have been viable? Could you operate every week in the same way based on the assumptions that were made?

This short course on cash flow planning is intended to introduce you to basic concepts for how to do a cash flow plan for your business. It focuses on preparing you to make *reasonable and realistic assumptions* about how and when cash will move in and out of your business.

If you have not dealt with business financial information before, you may want to seek assistance with the preparation of your cash flow plan.

It is *your responsibility* as a business owner to make these decisions and to figure things out. The assumptions you make *must be your own* – with guidance from people experienced in business operations and business planning. You will own and operate the business; therefore, you must make the business decisions.

Depending on who else will be reviewing your projections, you may be required to have them in GAAP (Generally Accepted Accounting Principles) format as directed by FASB (Financial Accounting Standards Board). A certified public accountant can assist you in compiling the projections in the proper format. The accountant's role will be to use your assumptions to format your cash flow plan in compliance with generally accepted accounting principles. This will not result in any changes to your assumptions.

At first, this work may seem confusing and frustrating. However, once you have done your homework, the cash flow plan will make sense to you.

People who can help you learn about your assumptions and things to consider when planning your business include business consultants, business owners, and people experienced in the detailed decision-making issues you will be learning about.

You may find a resource that offers computerized cash flow assistance. You make the assumptions. The service provider enters your assumptions on a computer spreadsheet. Then you can play the "what if" game by changing your assumptions and quickly seeing what the impact is on your ending cash. This is an excellent way for you to learn how the decisions you make will impact your cash flow.

If you have a computer with a spreadsheet program, you can create your own cash flow spreadsheet. It's easier than you might think, and instructions for the math and logic are included on the cash flow projection form at the end of this section.

"We'll have to either reduce operating costs or raise prices. Try this…"

CASH FLOW PLANNING

WHAT IS CASH FLOW?

Cash is the *fuel that powers a business*. Without cash, the business won't operate. Without enough cash when the business needs cash, the business will operate sporadically or sluggishly. If there is no cash, the business won't operate at all.

In either case, no cash or slow cash, the business owner will eventually lose income and/or investments.

Cash flow is a phrase used to describe the movement of *cash* in and out of a business. Cash flow specifically addresses:

- Timing – when cash moves in and out
- Amounts – how much cash moves in and out
- Sources – where cash comes from
- Uses – where cash goes
- Relationships – the relationships of business activity to producing or using cash

WHAT IS A CASH FLOW PLAN?

A cash flow plan is a financial plan that projects future sources and uses of cash in specific:

- Time periods
- Amounts
- Categories of sources and uses

WHAT DOES THE SUCCESSFUL CASH FLOW PLAN FOCUS ON?

- Financial goals (business and personal)
- Reality
- Timing

WHY DO CASH FLOW PLANNING?

1. To identify how much cash is needed and when. *
2. To set financial goals.
3. To measure and monitor business activities.
4. To evaluate and assess business strategies.
5. To make decisions about the future based on the activities of the past.
6. To identify cash weaknesses and cash strengths of the business.
7. To identify risks the business owner might take.
8. To identify rewards the business owner might receive.
9. Lenders require a cash flow plan.

*The more thorough your cash flow projections are, the better they will predict your business's need for cash. Show when you think cash will be received into the business and when cash will be needed to pay bills. It is easy to flat-line revenue and expenses. Flat-lining means that you have entered the exact same amount every month for the cash in or cash out item. The likelihood of this occurring is rare and is generally only when you have a commitment to pay a fixed monthly amount. Rent, for example, is the same amount every month. Any items that vary according to sales, such as purchases, will vary month-to-month.

BUSINESS FINANCIAL GOALS

PRIMARY BUSINESS FINANCIAL GOALS

The two primary business financial goals are:

1. For the business to be solvent (able to meet financial obligations). The business should produce enough cash to operate effectively and meet the needs of its customers.

2. For the business to produce enough cash to serve the owner's needs.

Remember, customers drive the business. A primary goal is to meet their needs. But why are you in business at all? The business must also produce enough cash to meet the owner's needs as well as the business needs. Both the business and the owner must receive enough cash to be solvent.

HOW TO SET BUSINESS FINANCIAL GOALS

In order to assure that the business will serve both masters – its customers and its owner – a well-thought-out business plan is essential. The marketing portion of the business plan will drive the cash flow decision-making.

1. Based on the results of the marketing plan, identify your sales goals, the *amount* of cash these sales will produce, and *when* the business will receive the cash.

2. Record this projected cash income as *sources* of cash on a business cash flow form.

3. Think about what your business will need in order to meet sales goals and your owner draw.

4. Identify the types and *amounts* of cash the business will spend and *when* it will spend the cash.

5. Record the cash your business will spend as *uses* on a business cash flow form.

6. Figure the difference between sources and *uses*.

7. If *uses* are greater than *sources*, the business does not have enough cash to meet its needs. Consider business adjustments that will result in either increasing your *sources* or decreasing your *uses*.

8. Take action to meet your business goals.

SOURCES		USES	
Owner	10,000	Equipment	15,000
ABC Bank	10,000	Inventory	12,000
City EDA	10,000	Working Capital	3,000
Total Sources	30,000	Total Uses	30,000

HOW DO YOU CREATE A CASH FLOW PLAN?

GO FIGURE!

The cash flow plan is not a simple fill-in-the-blanks form – it is a process. Your cash flow plan builds the foundation for all future decision-making about your business.

The cash flow plan is created during the process of business planning. The cash flow form is a "gathering tray" where you record the financial results of each of your business planning decisions.

BASIC CASH FLOW PLANNING STEPS

1. Identify the classifications for *sources* of cash.

2. Identify the classifications for *uses* of cash.

3. Think, research, analyze, calculate, decide:

    a) The amount of cash each item will produce or require, and

    b) When the cash will be received or spent.

4. Explain, in the form of notes, the method, logic, or resources you used to make <u>assumptions</u> about your business cash. (Example: Rent = $750/month.)

5. Record the results (dollars) on the cash flow form.

6. Calculate the totals on the cash flow form.

7. Review the results for validity and achievability.

8. Get feedback, critique, verification – test your theories.

9. Adjust or affirm the projection based on feedback and tests.

10. Monitor the projection and compare it with actual results.

11. Adjust your future projections as needed.

THINK, RESEARCH, ANALYZE, CALCULATE, DECIDE

In order to operate my restaurant I'll need a cook and two waiters during the noon and evening meal times during my "busy" time of year. I'll do all of the morning prep and cleanup.

I've researched and found that cooks are paid between $7 and $9 per hour, and waiters are paid about $5 per hour plus tips. I'll be closed on Sundays.

The cook will work from 10:00 a.m. to 7:00 p.m. with one hour for lunch and breaks. That's 8 hours per day at $7.00 per hour. That's $56 per day times 6 days per week. Let's see...that's $336 per week for the cook.

The waiters will work 4-hour shifts – from 10:30 a.m. to 2:30 p.m. and from 4:00 p.m. to 8:00 p.m. That's two waiters paid $5 per hour times 8 hours per day, plus their tips. That's $80 per day, or $480 per week.

So, for the two waiters and the cook, wages will be $816 per week from March through October. There are 4.33 weeks in a month. Per month, it will be $816 x 4.33 = $3,533.

In the winter, from November through February, I'll only need one waiter for six hours per day and I'll do all of the cooking, prep and cleanup. Let's see, that's one waiter times six hours at $5 per hour equals $30 per day or $180 per week from November through February. Per month, it will be $180 x 4.33, or a total of $779 per month.

Whew! OK. Now, I'll have to pay FICA and Medicare, and Workers' Compensation insurance, so I'd better find out how much that will cost.

I'll also have to pay unemployment taxes. Let's see, do I have to pay vacation time and sick pay? I'd better talk to someone and find out.

SUMMARIZE YOUR ASSUMPTIONS:

WAGES: Wages are calculated based on three full-time employees from March through October and one part-time employee from November through February.

PAYROLL TAXES: Payroll taxes include employer's FICA (6.2%), Medicare (1.45%), and state (5% - may vary by state) and federal unemployment compensation FUTA (0.08%), a total estimate of 12.73% of wages. Payroll taxes are paid quarterly except FUTA, which is paid annually.

WORKERS' COMPENSATION: Workers' Compensation is based on a quotation from Al's Reliable Insurance (copy attached as Exhibit C). The entire premium is due in the first month. An adjustment may be made at year-end. Additional amounts may be due or a refund returned based on actual employee hours.

RECORD THE RESULTS ON YOUR CASH FLOW FORM

Note: The jagged lines represent a split in the page displayed (actual page too large to fit in this space).

Description	Jan	Feb	Mar	Apr	Oct	Nov	Dec	Totals
Wages paid	780	780	3533	3533	3533	780	780	31,384
Payroll taxes owed	*99*	*99*	*450*	*450*	*450*	*99*	*99*	*3,995*

Although payroll taxes are owed as shown on the line above, they are not PAID until they are due, which in this example is in the month after the end of the quarter. The above line would not appear on a cash flow projection, since it is information about the amount of payroll taxes. The line below is about CASH used to pay payroll taxes.

Description	Jan	Feb	Mar	Apr	Oct	Nov	Dec	Totals
Payroll taxes paid				648	1434			3,347
Workers' Compensation	650							650

THEN ASK YOURSELF...

- What if cash from sales is not sufficient to operate the business?
- What will be my first line of defense if sales do not materialize as planned?
- Does my business require that I have a white Cadillac in order to sell insurance?
- Does my business really need to pay my cousin Phil $20 per hour?
- Does my business really need an 8,000 square foot showroom for dried flower arrangements?
- Will the business really produce eight million dollars in cash from sales in the first six months?
- Am I prepared to invest my life savings in this business?
- Could I realistically borrow $500,000?
- What will my cut-off date be? When will I decide to close the business if it is not as successful as I have planned?
- How sensitive is this projection to outside influences?

CORE FOUR® Business Planning Course

YOUR CASH FLOW PROJECTION IS A WORKING TOOL

The first edition of your cash flow projection will help you identify the feasibility of starting, expanding or continuing your business operation, and will help you identify what the needs of the business are. It will be the foundation from which all your future decisions are made, and you can adjust it accordingly.

PEOPLE HAVE FRIENDS, BUSINESSES HAVE CUSTOMERS

Offering discounts and special opportunities to friends and family dilutes your ability to serve your customers and dilutes your sources of cash.

Would you give your family and friends money out of your pocket? That's essentially what is happening when you give them special purchasing and employee advantages.

If the business needs employees, hire people who are qualified to serve your customers, and pay fair wages. If employees are family members, remember that for your business, they are employees and they should fulfill the expectations that the business has for any and all employees.

PEOPLE HAVE WANTS, BUSINESSES HAVE NEEDS

Businesses don't want anything.

If you want a white Cadillac because you think it would be neat, it belongs on your *personal* cash flow. The business doesn't *want* a white Cadillac unless perhaps it is a limousine service, in which case it might *need* a white Cadillac.

These examples are those that test our business focus and commitment. It's difficult to make these kinds of choices until we separate our *personal* needs and wants from the needs of the business.

Your customers don't care who your employees are, as long as those employees serve customers. Your customers don't care what kind of car you drive, unless they are likely to be passengers.

ASSUMPTIONS TO YOUR CASH FLOW PROJECTIONS

Assumptions (supposing or something supposed) are very important to the development of your cash flow projections. Assumptions are created and can be gathered as you research information and cost on each individual line item of your cash flow projection. Keep copies of the quotations or bids that you receive during your information gathering process. These quotes are the source of information you will note in your assumptions, the quote itself may be included as attachments to your business plan or a loan request. The sources of information may be as important as the information itself. If it were to be said that cash flow projections were no more than a guess, then consider how close your guess will be with your assumptions on real numbers. What impact would it have on your business?

If a category does not apply to your business, explain why in the assumptions. This will help the reader to understand this category has been reviewed and not forgotten or left out. The worksheets on the following pages are a guide for you; add categories that are appropriate to your business.

Refer back to page 35-SP for an example of assumptions.

As you work through each section of your cash flow projection follow the steps outlined on page 5-CFP "Basic Cash Flow Planning Steps" and read again the example about employees on page 5-CFP through 6-CFP.

PROJECTING STARTUP CASH

WHAT IS STARTUP CASH?

Startup cash is money that must be spent to become a business, *to build the structure of a business*. This includes purchases that must be made and expenses that must be paid for both before the business opens and for a short time during the initial operation of the business.

Startup cash includes all money that must be spent in order for you to establish the business site, purchase inventory and equipment, hire staff, develop an image and packaging, and purchase supplies that will be essential for the business to be ready to serve customers.

Startup cash is one step in determining the *feasibility* of your business idea. Can it become a business? Will you have access to all of the resources the business will need, including startup cash? If not, the idea is not feasible.

When identifying the costs of items your business will need, compare both *new* and *used* prices, if possible.

BOOTSTRAPPING

Bootstrapping is a phrase that describes a process of *staging* a business start. A business must earn and grow its way to success. Few businesses can start as, for example, a Wal-Mart or a General Motors. Both of these businesses earned and grew their way to success. Microsoft Corporation started in a garage, and the owners initially invested less than $1,000.

STAGING RISK

Everyone wants everything new, but reality sets in when you talk to lenders. Startup businesses, regardless of how the future may look, are very risky. Staging the risk by investing as little as *necessary* and getting what the *business needs* instead of what the *owner wants* are wise strategies. Lenders will scoff at an unrealistic pie-in-the-sky business plan. They will be look more closely at a reasonable startup with future plans for expansion. Be realistic.

The worksheet on the following page will help you identify the categories of startup cash you may need. Your task will be to figure exactly whether or not your business will need these types of cash, and how much cash will be needed for each category.

Assumption Worksheet—Startup Cash

Category	Who did you contact? Did you get a bid or a quote? Will equipment be new or used? When must these items be paid? How did you figure it out?	Amount NEW	Amount USED
Advertising and promotional literature			
Answering machine or service			
Beginning inventory			
Bookkeeping and accounting supplies			
Cash register			
Computer, printer, software, and supplies			
Desks, office furniture			
Display racks, shelving, cabinets			
FAX machine			
Grand or pre-opening advertising and promotion			
Installation and training fees for computer or equipment			
Insurance: business, liability, building, product, equipment			
Legal and accounting fees			
Licenses, permits, registrations, dues			
Office supplies			
Postage machine or startup postage			
Production and shop equipment			
Production and shop supplies			
Remodeling costs			
Rent (security deposit plus first and last month rent)			

STARTUP CASH ASSUMPTIONS WORKSHEET-CONTINUED			
Category	Who did you contact? Did you get a bid or a quote? Will equipment be new or used? When must these items be paid? How did you figure it out?	Amount NEW	Amount USED
Signs			
Stationery, business cards			
Telephones, cell phones, pagers			
Telephone installation and deposit costs			
Ten-key tape calculator			
Utilities – deposits and hookup			
Workers' Compensation insurance (partial or full payment?)			
Working capital (cash the business will need to purchase or produce inventory) until enough cash is generated by the business for purchases.	Total:		
Operating capital (cash the business will need to pay bills for non-inventory expenses) until enough cash is generated by the business for operations	Total:		
Working capital and operating capital are amounts calculated as a part of the "what if" exercises discussed under "sensitivity analysis" or "business plan analysis" on page 29-CFP.			

Cash Flow Projection: Startup Cash

See "Projecting Startup Cash" on page 8-CFP - 10-CFP

Using your assumptions, plot out your Cash Flow Projection. The startup column of your Cash Flow Projection usually will only appears in the first year. Generally you do not enter any "sales" in the startup column. The preceding pages contain a worksheet to help you develop and identify the line items, or types of costs you will need for your business start or expansion.

CASH FLOW PROJECTION FOR YEAR ENDING 12/31/20XX

Name: Business	START	Jan	Feb	Mar	Apr	May	Jun	Jul	Aug	Sept	Oct	Nov	Dec	TOTALS	% Sales
1 TOTAL SALES															
2															
3															
4															
5 TOTAL CASH IN FROM SALES															
6 CASH OUT FOR GOODS															
7															
8															
9 TOTAL CASH OUT FOR GOODS															
10 CASH OUT FOR OPERATIONS															
11 Workers' Compensation/health insurance															
12 Accounting/legal/professional services															
13 Advertising & promotions															
14 Internet Charges															
15 Bank, credit card charges															
16															
17 Ins-gen'l liab															
18 Misc.															
19 Office supplies															
20 Repairs & Maintenance															
21 Tax, licenses															
22 Telephone															
23 Electricity, Water & Sewer, Trash Removal															
24 TOTAL CASH OUT FOR OPERATIONS															
25 NET CASH FROM OPERATIONS															
26 OTHER CASH IN															
27 Loan proceeds - BANK															
28 Loan proceeds - Investor															
29 Loan proceeds - Microenterprise loan															
30 Owner contributions															
31															
32 TOTAL OTHER CASH IN															
33 OTHER CASH OUT															
34 Closing costs															
35 P&I Debt Service	1	1	1	1	1	1	1	1	1	1	1	1	1	1	
36 P&I Debt Service	1	1	1	1	1	1	1	1	1	1	1	1	1	1	
37 P&I Debt Service															
38 Owner Draw															
39 Taxes, on Owner Draw															
40															
41 Equipment															
42 Buildings															
43 tools, misc															
44 TOTAL OTHER CASH OUT															
45 NET CHANGE IN CASH															
46 BEGINNING CASH	1	1	1	1	1	1	1	1	1	1	1	1	1	1	
47 ENDING CASH BALANCE	1	1	1	1	1	1	1	1	1	1	1	1	1	1	
48															
49															

PROJECTING CASH FOR GOODS OR SERVICES

WHAT IS CASH FOR GOODS OR SERVICES?

Cash for goods or services are dollars that *must be spent* to purchase or produce the goods or services that the business sells. These costs are incurred *only because sales occur.* If the business has no sales, it will not need to purchase or produce goods or services. These costs are sometimes called variable costs because the costs of goods or services will *vary in relationship to the volume of sales* of the business.

Availability of cash for goods or services is a first step in determining the *viability* of your business idea. Can your business stay in business? Only if it has access to the cash and other resources it needs.

Cash for goods or services may also be referred to as COGS – "Cost of Goods (Services) Sold."

The worksheet on the following page will help you identify the categories of cash for goods or services your business will need. Your task will be to figure exactly whether or not your business will need these types of cash, and how much cash will be needed for each category.

Keep copies of the quotations that you receive, and include them as attachments in your business plan. The sources of your information may be as important as the information itself.

If a category does not apply to your business, explain why in the assumptions column. Add categories as appropriate for your business.

For any worksheet, use additional sheets as appropriate.

Assumption Worksheet—Cash for Goods or Services

Category	Who did you contact? Did you get a bid or a quote? Will equipment be new or used? When and how often must these items be paid? How did you figure it out?	Amount
Direct Labor - Employees who produce products or provide direct services to customers		
Employer's FICA		
Health Insurance		
Medicare		
Staff training		
Unemployment Insurance		
Vacation, holiday, and sick pay		
Wages		
Workers' Compensation		
Purchases of merchandise, material or parts for resale		
Beginning inventory		
Contract labor or services		
Freight in		
Freight out		
Production supplies		
Production waste disposal		
Warranty costs		
Selling expenses		
Commissions		
Royalties		

Cash Flow Projection: Cash for Goods or Services

CASH FLOW PROJECTION FOR YEAR ENDING 12/31/20XX

Name: _____
Business

#		START	Jan	Feb	Mar	Apr	May	Jun	Jul	Aug	Sept	Oct	Nov	Dec	TOTALS	% Sales
1	TOTAL SALES															
2																
3																
4																
5	TOTAL CASH IN FROM SALES															
6	CASH OUT FOR GOODS															
7																
8																
9	TOTAL CASH OUT FOR GOODS															
10	CASH OUT FOR OPERATIONS															
11	Workers' Compensation/health insurance															
12	Accounting/legal/professional services															
13	Advertising & promotions															
14	Internet Charges															
15	Bank, credit card charges															
16																
17	Ins-gen'l liab															
18	Misc.															
19	Office supplies															
20	Repairs & Maintenance															
21	Tax, licenses															
22	Telephone															
23	Electricity, Water & Sewer, Trash Removal															
24	TOTAL CASH OUT FOR OPERATIONS															
25	NET CASH FROM OPERATIONS															
26	OTHER CASH IN															
27	Loan proceeds - BANK															
28	Loan proceeds - Investor															
29	Loan proceeds - Microenterprise loan															
30	Owner contributions															
31																
32	TOTAL OTHER CASH IN															
33	OTHER CASH OUT															
34	Closing costs															
35	P&I Debt Service															
36	P&I Debt Service															
37	P&I Debt Service															
38	Owner Draw															
39	Taxes, on Owner Draw															
40																
41	Equipment															
42	Buildings															
43	tools, misc															
44	TOTAL OTHER CASH OUT															
45	NET CHANGE IN CASH															
46	BEGINNING CASH	1	1	1	1	1	1	1	1	1	1	1	1	1		
47	ENDING CASH BALANCE	1	1	1	1	1	1	1	1	1	1	1	1	1		
48																
49																

"Cash out for Goods" section on pages 12-CFP - 13-CFP

Cash out for Goods or Cost of Goods (COG's) are the goods or services a business must buy (usually at wholesale) to provide for its customers (at retail). Examples: in a muffler repair shop both the muffler and the labor are considered COG's. In a gift shop, all the gift inventory are considered COG's. The key point to remember is to maintain or increase your inventory each month. In other words, allow for enough money from sales to replace your inventory.

CORE FOUR® Business Planning Course

PROJECTING CASH FOR OPERATIONS

WHAT IS CASH FOR OPERATIONS?

Cash for operations is cash the business has *committed* to pay in order to operate the business and to sustain the structure of the business, *whether or not the business has sales.*

Availability of cash for operations is a second step in determining the *viability* of your business idea. Can your business stay in business? Only if it has access to the cash and other resources it needs.

Operating cash is used for costs that are also called operating expenses, and are often called the costs of doing business.

Some operating costs are *fixed* costs. This does not mean they are the same every month. It means that the business is committed to paying these costs in order to be open and ready for business.

Operating costs may vary from month to month, but generally not because of sales. Heating and cooling costs, for example, vary according to the season. However, the business has committed to pay those costs in order to sustain the structure of the business, whether or not the business has sales. It will generally cost about the same to light the building for a year whether or not the business has sales.

Many operating costs are *recurring costs*, and include many of the same categories as startup costs:

Rent is a recurring expense. The startup portion is the deposit plus first and last month rent. The recurring portion is the monthly rent payment. The rent must be paid in order to sustain the business site. If the rent is not paid, the business will not have a business site.

Advertising is a recurring cost. The startup portion is the amount spent on a grand opening promotion and advertising literature. The recurring portion is the advertising done on behalf of the business throughout the year. The business may spend more money on advertising in some months than in others, but the business must commit to advertise in order to sustain the structure of the business.

The worksheet on the following page will help you identify the categories of cash for operations your business will incur. Your task is to figure exactly whether or not your business will need these types of cash, and how much cash will be needed for each category.

Keep copies of the quotations that you receive, and include them as attachments in your business plan. The sources of your information may be as important as the information itself.

If a category does not apply to your business, explain why in the assumptions column. Add categories as appropriate for your business.

For any worksheet, use additional sheets as appropriate.

Assumption Worksheet—Cash for Operations

Category	Who did you contact? Did you get a bid or a quote? How did you figure it out? When and how often (weekly, monthly, annually) is the cost paid? Is the cost seasonal?	Amount
Indirect Labor - Employees who do not produce products or provide direct services to customers		
Employer's FICA		
Health Insurance		
Medicare		
Staff training		
Temporary help		
Unemployment Insurance		
Vacation, holiday, and sick pay		
Wages		
Workers' Compensation		
Facility expenses		
Maintenance		
Real estate taxes		
Rent or lease payments		
Property insurance		
Utilities		

CASH ASSUMPTIONS FOR OPERATIONS WORKSHEET - CONTINUED		
Category	Who did you contact? Did you get a bid or a quote? How did you figure it out? When and how often (weekly, monthly, annually) is the cost paid? Is the cost seasonal?	Amount
General and administrative costs		
Accounting fees		
Advertising and promotion		
Consulting fees		
Contributions		
Dues		
Insurance, hazard and liability		
Legal fees		
Lease payments, equipment		
Licenses, permits		
Memberships		
Office supplies		
Postage		
Subscriptions		
Telephone		
Trash removal		
Travel and entertainment		
Vehicle expenses		

Cash Flow Projection: Operations

CASH FLOW PROJECTION FOR YEAR ENDING — 12/31/20XX

Name: _____
Business: _____

#	Row	START	Jan	Feb	Mar	Apr	May	Jun	Jul	Aug	Sept	Oct	Nov	Dec	TOTALS	% Sales
1	TOTAL SALES															
2																
3																
4																
5	TOTAL CASH IN FROM SALES															
6	CASH OUT FOR GOODS															
7																
8																
9	TOTAL CASH OUT FOR GOODS															
10	CASH OUT FOR OPERATIONS															
11	Workers' Compensation/health insurance															
12	Accounting/legal/professional services															
13	Advertising & promotions															
14	Internet Charges															
15	Bank, credit card charges															
16																
17	Ins-gen'l liab															
18	Misc.															
19	Office supplies															
20	Repairs & Maintenance															
21	Tax, licenses															
22	Telephone															
23	Electricity, Water & Sewer, Trash Removal															
24	TOTAL CASH OUT FOR OPERATIONS															
25	NET CASH FROM OPERATIONS															
26	OTHER CASH IN															
27	Loan proceeds - BANK															
28	Loan proceeds - Investor															
29	Loan proceeds - Microenterprise loan															
30	Owner contributions															
31																
32	TOTAL OTHER CASH IN															
33	OTHER CASH OUT															
34	Closing costs															
35	P&I Debt Service															
36	P&I Debt Service															
37	P&I Debt Service															
38	Owner Draw															
39	Taxes, on Owner Draw															
40																
41	Equipment															
42	Buildings															
43	tools, misc															
44	TOTAL OTHER CASH OUT															
45	NET CHANGE IN CASH															
46	BEGINNING CASH	1	1	1	1	1	1	1	1	1	1	1	1	1	1	
47	ENDING CASH BALANCE	1	1	1	1	1	1	1	1	1	1	1	1	1	1	
48																
49																

See "Projecting Cash for Operations" on pages 15-CFP - 17-CFP

Cash for Operations are all the fixed costs, the operational costs of running your business. Examples include rent, credit card machine, cell phone, salaries & wages, auto expenses, and tax on wages to mention a few. The worksheets on the preceding pages were used to identify your operational costs.

PROJECTING SALES

Projecting sales is the financial planning task that requires the most thought, attention, and effort.

With careful planning, it is not a mystical "wish" that your business achieve "enough sales."

Projecting sales realistically requires that you have your feet firmly planted on the ground.

Sales projections are critically studied and questioned by everyone who reviews your business plan. If sales projections appear unreasonable to potential lenders, vendors, or other resources, you may not be able to gather the support the business needs. If sales projections are not achievable, you are putting the investments of your time and money at risk.

KEY COMPONENTS OF SALES PROJECTIONS

Pricing – Pricing is a critical component of your marketing strategy. A common mistake business owners make is to establish prices that are lower than people would ordinarily pay, or that are lower than a competitor charges, "because I'm just starting up." Your attitude and knowledge really count here. If you get greedy and your prices are too high, your products and services will be priced out of the market. If you sell yourself short and underprice, your products and services will be devalued.

The "science" of pricing is using a cash breakeven analysis to determine if prices make sense.

Market analysis – The market analysis activities you perform for your business planning should give you information on the size and location of the market for your products or services, who your customers will be, how many of them there are, and how much they are likely to spend for what you offer.

Capacity – Every business has a limited capacity of both time and money. There are a fixed number of hours in the day during which work can be done. There is a limited amount of money available for inventory purchases.

Seasonality – Every business has seasonality. Sales will occur irregularly during the year, with higher sales in some months than in others. Some businesses make few sales Monday through Friday, with most sales on weekends. Some businesses have most sales Monday through Friday.

BREAKEVEN METHOD FOR PROJECTING SALES

Figure out how much sales *must* be to generate sufficient cash to cash flow the business and pay you your owner draw. Then determine how to achieve that level of sales. Then decide if it's worth it for you to try the business idea. This is the most practical method that will result in the most realistic sales projections.

However, you want to be sure to project breakeven sales to *cash flow the business* instead of breakeven sales to be *profitable*.

There are all kinds of businesses that are marginally or significantly profitable, but that do not have enough *cash* to stay in business.

Assumption Worksheet--Sales

In every business, sales will vary for reasons that can include the seasonal use of the product or service, the number of days per month, holidays, conflicting events and the weather. Sales can vary by time of day or day of the week. As you research your business idea and develop your marketing plan, you will learn about sales variations from industry research, potential customers, and other business owners. Recording the variations will help you identify your customers' shopping patterns and when your business will have cash available/need cash for operations. The more you understand the potential variations, the better you will be able to predict inventory and staffing, along with other expense categories that will vary with sales.

Based on your research, you will make assumptions for each category for of product or service you plan to offer. How many sales will you make each day, week or month? How much is an average sale? What are the terms of the sale? If it is not cash or credit card, when will you receive payment? You will want to account for the time delay in your projections. What does it cost to produce goods or services sold? How frequently will your customers purchase and when?

Month	1	2	3	4	5	6	7	8	9	10	11	12
Product/Service #1												
Number of sales												
Average sale												
Cost to produce												
Cash received												
Product/Service #2												
Number of sales												
Average sale												
Cost to produce												
Cash received												
Product/Service #3												
Number of sales												
Average sale												
Cost to produce												
Cash received												

Cash Flow Projection: Sales

CASH FLOW PROJECTION FOR YEAR ENDING — 12/31/20XX

Name: _____
Business: _____

See "Projecting Sales" on pages CFP-19 - CFP-20.

Once you have priced your product or service, go back into your marketing plan and figure out how often those customers you have identified will come to your business per month, and how much they will spend each visit. If you have a store that has four different items or departments, it may be easier to list each of them on a separate line. Remember to show the "seasonality" of your sales.

#		START	Jan	Feb	Mar	Apr	May	Jun	Jul	Aug	Sept	Oct	Nov	Dec	TOTALS	% Sales
1	TOTAL SALES															
2																
3																
4																
5	TOTAL CASH IN FROM SALES															
6	CASH OUT FOR GOODS															
7																
8																
9	TOTAL CASH OUT FOR GOODS															
10	CASH OUT FOR OPERATIONS															
11	Workers' Compensation/health insurance															
12	Accounting/legal/professional services															
13	Advertising & promotions															
14	Internet Charges															
15	Bank, credit card charges															
16																
17	Ins-gen'l liab															
18	Misc.															
19	Office supplies															
20	Repairs & Maintenance															
21	Tax, licenses															
22	Telephone															
23	Electricity, Water & Sewer, Trash Removal															
24	TOTAL CASH OUT FOR OPERATIONS															
25	NET CASH FROM OPERATIONS															
26	OTHER CASH IN															
27	Loan proceeds - BANK															
28	Loan proceeds - Investor															
29	Loan proceeds - Microenterprise loan															
30	Owner contributions															
31																
32	TOTAL OTHER CASH IN															
33	OTHER CASH OUT															
34	Closing costs															
35	P&I Debt Service		1	1	1	1	1	1	1	1	1	1	1	1		
36	P&I Debt Service		1	1	1	1	1	1	1	1	1	1	1	1		
37	P&I Debt Service															
38	Owner Draw															
39	Taxes, on Owner Draw															
40																
41	Equipment															
42	Buildings															
43	tools, misc															
44	TOTAL OTHER CASH OUT															
45	NET CHANGE IN CASH															
46	BEGINNING CASH	1	1	1	1	1	1	1	1	1	1	1	1	1		
47	ENDING CASH BALANCE	1	1	1	1	1	1	1	1	1	1	1	1	1		
48																
49																

HOW TO PROJECT SALES USING THE CASH BREAKEVEN METHOD

It may seem very complex. Let's simplify this.

Let's start a pie bakery. We know that it will cost $3 to make each pie. We know that we want to sell each pie for $9.50.

9.50	net cash from sales
(3.00)	cash for purchases
6.50	cash after sales
6.50 divided by 9.50 = .68, or 68%	
68%	**gross profit margin**

Okay, we've also figured out that it will cost us $34,000 per year to operate our bakery. That includes our owner draw of $16,000.

What are our breakeven sales? (Cash for operations and owner draw is total cash out.)

$34,000 divided by 68% = $50,000.

Our annual sales must be $50,000 in order for us to draw $16,000 in cash for ourselves and have cash to operate the business as well.

That sounds like a lot of pies. How many is it per year? Total sales of $50,000 divided by $9.50 per pie equals 5,264 pies.

That really sounds like a lot of pies.

Hmmm. How many is that per week?

5264 divided by 52 weeks = 102 pies per week.

Okay, that sounds not quite so bad. How many pies is that per day? I only want to bake pies 5 days per week.

102 pies per week divided by 5 days = 21 pies per day.

We must sell 21 pies per day, 5 days per week, 52 weeks per year, at $9.50 each, in order for us to operate our bakery and draw $16,000.

There are many methods used for projecting sales, but the cash breakeven method is the most realistic and practical. It helps you identify what your business *must* sell in order to have enough cash to pay all of its bills *and* to pay you.

The worksheet on the following page will help you calculate your cash breakeven. Your task will be to figure exactly, using every and any sensitivity, marketing, or operations planning tool, how likely it is that your business can achieve this level of sales, and what your business will have to do to achieve it.

You may be familiar with other methods for projecting sales. You have heard the word "profit" before. If you focus on profits instead of cash, the likelihood that you may have circumstances in your business where you will not have enough cash to pay bills is very high.

Worksheet—Sales to Cash Breakeven

Examples A and B are for the same business, but _two different business owners_. Who did a better job of managing the business? In Example B, what advice do you have for the business owner? Discuss the results of each "sales required" and how the owner can make profitable changes.

Description	YOUR BUSINESS	EXAMPLE A	EXAMPLE B
Total sales		$175,000	$103,221
Less returns and allowances _(refunds and discounts)_		-4890.00	-2890.00
Less accounts receivable _(money your customers owe your business)_		-21,412.00	-31,412.00
Net cash from sales		**148,698.00**	**68,919.00**
Less cash for purchases _(goods purchased for resale)_		-53,442.00	-41,883.00
Cash after sales		**95, 256.00**	**27,036.00**
Gross profit margin % _(Cash after sales divided by net cash from sales)0_		**64%**	**39%**
Cash for operations		43,545.00	43,545.00
Cash for owner draw		26,000.00	26,000.00
Other cash out _(debt service, capital purchases)_		18,599.00	18,599.00
Total cash out		**88,144.00**	**88,144.00**
Sales required to cash breakeven _(Total cash out divided by gross profit margin %)_		**$137,725.00**	**$226,010.25**

CASH AND PROFITS ARE NOT THE SAME

Profit is a formula used to determine income tax liability, and it is *financial information*. If we did not have to pay taxes, we would not calculate profits.

Cash is cash. Cash planning is information about money. Period.

Huh?

1 + 1 = 3

We know that 1 + 1 does not equal three. We know that 1 + 1 = 2. Don't we?

But sometimes… depending on exactly just how you look at things… could 1 + 1 = 3?

To truly understand the difference between profits and cash, you may need some accounting experience to grasp the difference in your brain.

But you will not need any experience to grasp the difference in your pocketbook.

So if the business is so profitable…

Where's my money?

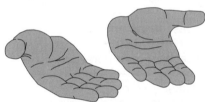

The example on the following pages presents a comparison of profit and profit breakeven versus cash and cash breakeven.

CALCULATING PROFITS VERSUS ENDING CASH

These simplified profit and cash calculations are based on the *same business* for the *same year*. They present two different ways of looking at the same events that occurred during the year for this business.

PROFIT CALCULATION				ENDING CASH CALCULATION		
Total sales	397,742		**1**	Total sales	397,742	
Less returns & allowances	(1,442)		**2**	Less returns & allowances	(1,442)	
Net sales		396,300	**3**	Net sales	396,300	
			4	**Less accounts receivable**	**(22,571)**	
			5	Net cash from sales		373,729
Less cost of goods sold			**6**			
Beginning inventory	42,843		**7**			
Plus purchases for resale	240,252		**8**	Less purchases for resale		(240,252)
Less ending inventory	(43,746)		**9**			
Total cost of goods sold	239,349	(239,349)	**10**			
Operating expenses		(105,739)	**11**	Cash for operations		(105,739)
NET PROFIT		**51,212**	**12**	CASH FROM OPERATIONS		27,738
			13	**OTHER CASH OUT**		
			14	Equipment purchased	2,117	
			15	Loan principal paid	4,633	
			16	Owner's self employment tax 15.03% of NET PROFIT	7,697	
			17	Owner's income tax based on NET PROFIT as adjusted gross income	1,149	
			18	Cash for one month of operating expenses so the business can stay in business	8,812	
			19	Cash to buy more inventory after year-end	20,000	
			20	**Total other cash out**		**(44,408)**
			21	Beginning cash (*cash the business had at the beginning of the year*)		4,321
			22	**Ending cash BEFORE owner draw**	Uh Oh!	**(12,349)**

Let's run the breakeven on each of the examples above and see what it tells us. Remember in a break-even analysis we want to know if the projected sales will be enough to pay <u>for everything</u> we want the business to accomplish. What we want the business to accomplish comes from our goals.

PROFIT BREAKEVEN VERSUS CASH BREAKEVEN

PROFIT BREAKEVEN CALCULATION

Net sales	396,300	
Cost of goods sold	(239,349)	
Gross profit	156,951	
Gross profit margin (gross profit divided by net sales) 156951 divided by 396300 = .40		40%
Operating expenses		105,739
Profit breakeven (operating expenses divided by gross margin %) 105,739 divided by .40 =		264,348
SALES REQUIRED TO PROFIT BREAKEVEN		**264,348**

CASH BREAKEVEN CALCULATION

Net cash from sales	373,729	
Cash for purchases	(240,252)	
Cash after sales	133,477	
Cash margin (cash after sales, divided by net cash from sales) 133477 divided by 373729 = .36		36%
Cash for operations	105,739	
All other cash out	44,408	
Owner draw	24,000	
Total cash out		174,147
Cash breakeven formula = (total cash out divided by cash margin %) 174,147 divided by .36 =		483,742
SALES REQUIRED TO CASH BREAKEVEN		**483,742**

It's not exactly the difference between 1 + 1 = 3 and 1 + 1 = 2, but the point is clearly demonstrated. *Profits and cash are not the same.*

Which sales level will be easier to achieve? Which sales level must this business achieve to cash flow?

BREAKEVEN ANALYSIS

As a business owner, you need to know your breakeven point – the level of sales at which your costs will be covered. If sales do not reach breakeven, you will not be able to pay all of your bills. If sales exceed breakeven, you will have enough money to pay for everything you wish to do in the business. (As we saw in the example on the previous page, "money to pay for everything" should include owner draw, additional equipment, building inventory, and paying your loan – your "wish list" of everything you want your business to accomplish.) The graph below assumes a constant cost of $50,000 (solid line) for sales from $0 to $115,000 (marked line). If sales are less than $50,000 the business will have lost money. If sales exceed $50,000 the business will have the cash to pay for those extra items on your "wish list." If sales do not reach breakeven, you will need to determine sources of working capital to get you through the month.

Breakeven Analysis

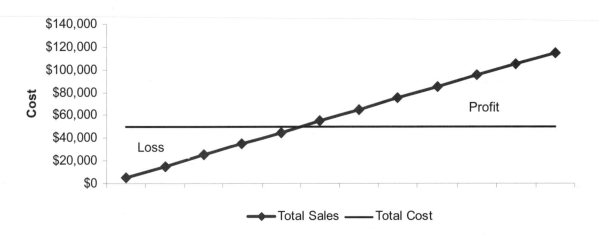

Cash Breakeven Example: The Pie Bakery and Brilliant Cleaning Service

Remember the Pie Bakery back on page 22-CFP? We first figured out the cost of each pie. We calculated the cost of operating the pie bakery and identified the amount to take home as owner draw.

Then we analyzed our assumptions by calculating the number of pies to make each day. Our conclusion was:

We must sell 21 pies per day, 5 days per week, 52 weeks per year, at $9.50 each, in order for us to operate our bakery and draw $16,000.

Refer back to the sample business plans in the Success Planning section of this book.

Review the cash flow projections for Brilliant Cleaning Service on pages 33-SP – 34-SP to see how the numbers enter into the following cash breakeven example below.

THE PIE BAKERY

Description	YEAR ONE
Total sales	$50,000
Less returns and allowances *(refunds and discounts)*	0
Less accounts receivable *(money your customers owe your business)*	0
Net cash from sales	**50,000**
Less cash for purchases *(goods purchased for resale)*	-16,000
Cash after sales	**34,000**
Gross profit margin % *(Cash after sales divided by net cash from sales)*	**68%**
Cash for operations	18,000
Cash for owner draw	16,000
Other cash out *(debt service, capital purchases)*	0
Total cash out	**34,000**
Sales required to cash breakeven *(Total cash out divided by gross profit margin %)*	**50,000**

BRILLIANT CLEANING SERVICE

Description	20YY
Total sales	$21,510
Less returns and allowances *(refunds and discounts)*	0
Less accounts receivable *(money your customers owe your business)*	0
Net cash from sales	**21,510**
Less cash for purchases *(goods purchased for resale)*	475
Cash after sales	**21,035**
Gross profit margin % *(Cash after sales divided by net cash from sales)*	**98%**
Cash for operations	3,725
Cash for owner draw	16,560
Other cash out *(debt service, capital purchases)*	780
Total cash out	**21,065**
Sales required to cash breakeven *(Total cash out divided by gross profit margin %)*	**21,495**

Cash Breakeven Worksheet: Scrapbook Nook

Refer to the cash flow projections for the Scrapbook Nook (pages 47-48 SP) to complete the cash breakeven worksheet below.

SCRAPBOOK NOOK

Cash Breakeven Analysis	YEAR ONE	YEAR TWO
Total sales	$55,855	
Less returns and allowances *(refunds and discounts)*	0	
Less accounts receivable *(money your customers owe your business)*	0	
Net cash from sales	**55,855**	
Less cash for purchases *(goods purchased for resale)*	26,638	
Cash after sales	**29,217**	
Gross profit margin % *(Cash after sales divided by net cash from sales)*	**52%**	
Cash for operations	8,670	
Cash for owner draw	3,100	
Other cash out *(debt service, capital purchases)*	7,650	
Total cash out	**19,420**	
Sales required to cash breakeven *(Total cash out divided by gross profit margin %)*	37,346	

BUSINESS PLAN ANALYSIS

The sensitivity analysis is a complex way of saying:

Figure out if this can really happen.
Figure out if we can sell 21 pies each day.

We figure it out by asking questions and getting as much verification and validation as we can about the assumptions we have made.

How many people will buy our pies? How often? Where else can they get pies? Do our price and quality make sense to consumers? Can we even make 21 pies each day? Do we want to?

The sensitivity analysis is where your market planning knowledge is critical, and where you apply your good common sense and market research to evaluate whether or not your sales goals are achievable.

Your packaging and promotion strategies are where you apply your knowledge of the marketplace to entice 21 people each day to buy your pies.

Your operations planning strategies are where you make sure that your costs for operating do not exceed $34,000 per year, and the costs of each pie do not exceed $3.

Sensitivity analysis is asking questions:

What if there is a "pie glut" in the marketplace and the selling price of pies drops to $6?

What if we don't sell 21 pies each day? What can we do?

What if we don't have the capacity to make 21 pies each day?

What if we decide that making 21 pies, 5 days per week, 52 weeks per year doesn't sound like a good time?

What if the cost of making a pie increases to $3.50 per pie? How will it affect our sales?

What if. …what if…. what if…. ?

Sensitivity is looking at your projections upside down and sideways, inside and out. Asking anyone who knows anything about the pie business if your projections make sense, if they can offer any "what if?" questions.

And now we're done projecting sales!

Ah… maybe not. I just figured out that we would hardly sell any pies in November through March, because the tourist population drops to nearly zero.

Guess we'll have to refigure a few things.

PROJECTING OTHER SOURCES AND USES OF CASH

Other sources and uses of cash include purchasing *assets* (things you own), incurring *liabilities* (debts you owe), and *owner contributions*.

ASSETS

The business can use cash to purchase assets.

- When will the business need additional equipment?
- When will the business need a photocopier?
- When will the business need a computer?

The business can receive cash by selling assets.

- We found out we have to contract the painting of our product because we're not zoned for this type of work. We're going to sell the paint booth, compressor and supplies.

LIABILITIES

The business can receive cash by borrowing money:

- In order to get started, we have to borrow $10,000.

Or use cash to pay debt:

- Our monthly principal payments will be $395 for six years.

OWNER CONTRIBUTIONS

The business can receive cash from you, the owner.

- I have invested $6,359 in equipment and supplies, which I will contribute to the business.

- I will also invest $7,000 of my own cash to get started.

Other sources and uses of cash also include other income and expenses *indirectly* related to the operation of the business.

Below are listed various types of other sources and uses of cash.

These types of sources and uses of cash are generally projected after you complete the proforma, the initial version, of your cash flow projection.

OTHER SOURCES OF CASH

Advertising rebates
Bad debt recovery
Deposits refunded
Finance charges earned
Insurance refunds
Interest earned
Payroll reimbursement plans
Sales tax collected

OTHER USES OF CASH

Finance charges paid
Interest paid
Sales tax paid

Cash Flow Projection: Other Cash In/Other Cash Out

CASH FLOW PROJECTION FOR YEAR ENDING 12/31/20XX

Name:
Business

#		START	Jan	Feb	Mar	Apr	May	Jun	Jul	Aug	Sept	Oct	Nov	Dec	TOTALS	% Sales
1	TOTAL SALES															
2																
3																
4																
5	TOTAL CASH IN FROM SALES															
6	CASH OUT FOR GOODS															
7																
8																
9	TOTAL CASH OUT FOR GOODS															
10	CASH OUT FOR OPERATIONS															
11	Workers' Compensation/health insurance															
12	Accounting/legal/professional services															
13	Advertising & promotions															
14	Internet Charges															
15	Bank, credit card charges															
16																
17	Ins-gen'l liab															
18	Misc.															
19	Office supplies															
20	Repairs & Maintenance															
21	Tax, licenses															
22	Telephone															
23	Electricity, Water & Sewer, Trash Removal															
24	TOTAL CASH OUT FOR OPERATIONS															
25	NET CASH FROM OPERATIONS															
26	OTHER CASH IN															
27	Loan proceeds - BANK															
28	Loan proceeds - Investor															
29	Loan proceeds - Microenterprise loan															
30	Owner contributions															
31																
32	TOTAL OTHER CASH IN															
33	OTHER CASH OUT															
34	Closing costs															
35	P&I Debt Service															
36	P&I Debt Service															
37	P&I Debt Service															
38	Owner Draw															
39	Taxes, on Owner Draw															
40																
41	Equipment															
42	Buildings															
43	tools, misc															
44	TOTAL OTHER CASH OUT															
45	NET CHANGE IN CASH															
46	BEGINNING CASH	1	1	1	1	1	1	1	1	1	1	1	1	1		
47	ENDING CASH BALANCE	1	1	1	1	1	1	1	1	1	1	1	1	1		
48																
49																

"Other Cash In" is the injection of cash from yourbank loan, economic development loan, microenterprise loan, and your contribution. "Notes" or loans from Mom or shareholders will go in this section as well. The loan section is typically the last section you fill in, after you know all your other costs for startup or expansion.

"Other Cash Out" is where you list the owner draw, loan payments, the equipment your business needs, maybe the building you are buying and any of the "non-operating" and "one time" costs of starting or expanding this business. You may even project buying additional equipment in eight months or increasing your owner draw in one year.

HOW MUCH MONEY DO YOU NEED TO START YOUR BUSINESS?

Enough. Not too much. Not too little. Perhaps none at all.

Easy to say. Surprisingly, easy to figure out as well. These are the rules and techniques:

1. Do not predetermine how much money you think you need. Let the "numbers talk." Your cash flow projection will identify how much money you need.

2. Prepare a thoughtful, comprehensive cash flow projection. "Operate" your business on paper.

3. Start your business or project with zero money as "beginning cash." If you already have a specific amount of cash available for starting your business or project, include that specific amount as "beginning cash."

4. Calculate the cash flow. It is likely that you will have negative cash for several months until cash generated from sales begins to flow in.

5. On your cash flow projection, find the month that has the largest amount of negative cash.

   This is the amount of money, plus interest and borrowing costs, your business will need.

   Subsequent months may have negative cash as well, but the negative amount will begin to decrease as your business begins to increase its cash flow from sales and operations.

Remember the very first exercise at the beginning of this book, where you planned your weekly personal fund? What was the largest negative number during the week? On what day?

This number is the amount of additional money (plus interests and borrowing costs) you would have needed if you chose to operate the week according to the plan presented.

WHERE SHOULD YOU GET THE MONEY?

It depends. Can you borrow it? Do you have sufficient collateral and good credit? You may be able to go to a bank. Commercial lenders lend money based on their analysis of the potential for failure. If you fail to pay the loan, they can repossess your collateral and sell it to cover their debt. If you have a good credit history, they consider it, in part, a secondary source of repayment. A good credit history verifies and validates that you have taken your debts seriously and paid them.

Do you not have sufficient collateral, or a less than perfect credit history? A non-traditional lender may be a choice for you. They analyze your potential for success. Since you do not have sufficient collateral that could be liquidated in the event you don't repay the debt, the only option is to validate and verify your opportunities for success.

DUE DILIGENCE

How can your opportunities for success be verified and validated by a stranger – a prospective lender or investor? By reading your business plan, studying your cash flow projections, talking to you, doing their homework. This process is called *due diligence*.

Due diligence is the process of verifying and validating, whenever possible with third-parties, that the assumptions and declarations you are making have a reasonable opportunity for success.

PROJECTED SOURCES AND USES OF FUNDS

The type of form on the following page is prepared by lenders to analyze the relationship between where the cash is coming from and what the cash will be used for.

Lenders perform their own due diligence, and relationships of sources and uses are very important to them.

If all of the money for a startup or expansion is borrowed, and the owner has made no contributions, who is taking all of the risk?

If a loan of $50,000 is being requested, and there is no security for the loan in the form of assets, who has something to lose?

Your projected cash flow will be critical to "selling" the success of your business to a lender.

The more thought, time and energy you put into this effort, the greater the reward.

You will have "figured out" how to achieve your dream, or you will have taken risk "on paper," and determined that your dream could be a nightmare instead.

The process of revising your cash flow, changing your mind, altering your plan, and letting the numbers "talk" the language of business to you will help you understand the choices you have.

You can "step" yourself into business by taking *calculated risks*. You can "leap" yourself into business by taking great risks.

You can decide that you don't want to do this business at all.

In any case, you will have made your choices based on logic and planning, instead of wishing and hoping.

Projected Sources and Uses of Funds Form

Business Name:			Compiled by:		Date:	
SOURCES OF FUNDS			**USES OF FUNDS**			
DEBT			**CURRENT ASSETS**			
Lender #1			Inventory for resale			
Lender #2			Supplies inventory			
Lender #3			Prepaid expenses			
Lessor #1						
Lessor #2			**Total current assets**			
Lessor #3			**FIXED ASSETS**			
			Land			
			Building purchase			
Total debt			Building improvements			
EQUITY			Leasehold improvements			
Owner cash contribution			Equipment purchased			
Owner non-cash contribution			Equipment leased			
Investor #1			Furniture & fixtures			
Investor #2						
Investor #3						
			Total fixed assets			
			Total assets			
Total equity			**STARTUP EXPENSES**			
			WORKING CAPITAL			
TOTAL SOURCES OF FUNDS			**TOTAL USES OF FUNDS**			

DESCRIPTION OF DEBTS:

Lender = D Lessor = S	Term (length of loan or lease)	Interest or lease rate (percent)	Secured by (collateral)	Total amount borrowed	Monthly payments

DESCRIPTION OF EQUITY:

Owner/investor	Relationship	Percent ownership or terms of investment

CASH FLOW PROJECTION WORKSHEET

The cash flow projection worksheet on the following pages can be used as your "gathering tray" where you record the cash results of your financial decisions.

Tips:

- Get feedback! Always be willing to discuss your plans with your advisors. Ask for and listen to their feedback.

- If your business will not have a specific cash out or cash in category that is already described on the form, indicate in your written assumptions that the item is not applicable to your business.

- If you need to add other categories, cross off the ones that you won't be using, or combine two categories, or use additional sheets.

- Number your written assumptions to correspond to the numbers of the line items on the cash flow projection form. This will help someone reading your plan to identify which assumption goes with which line item. It will help you track them as well.

- Write your initial entries in pencil. Write clearly and with a bold hand. Erase or draw a line through entries that have changed (rather than write over numbers that you have previously recorded).

- Do not use pennies when entering the data on this form. Round the numbers up or down, as appropriate. It will greatly simplify the math and readability of your projection.

- Do not flat-line revenue or expenses unless you can validate that they will be the same every month. Flat-lining means that you have entered the same amount every month for the cash in or cash out item. Sales, however, will vary each month based on seasonality, industry fluctuations, holidays, and other factors. Any categories that vary according to sales, such as COGS, will also vary each month.

- *Verify* and *validate* your assumptions with *written* quotations from your vendors, or *factual* data from other third-party sources. Include copies of written validations in your business plan.

- When cash in or out is paid or received sporadically, draw a "window" in the column where the amount should be recorded. For example, payroll taxes for many small businesses can be deposited quarterly instead of every month. On the line for payroll taxes, draw a "window" in the appropriate month columns to remind yourself that these are the months in which the taxes should be paid.

- Cash out examples:

	JAN	FEB	MAR	APR	MAY	JUN	JUL	AUG	SEP	OCT	NOV	DEC
Payroll taxes	☐			☐			☐			☐		
Liability Insurance			☐						☐			
Workers Comp			☐									

- Cash in examples:

	JAN	FEB	MAR	APR	MAY	JUN	JUL	AUG	SEP	OCT	NOV	DEC
Owner contribution			☐						☐			
Loan proceeds			☐									

					STARTUP	JAN		FEB		MAR		APR		MAY	
Business Name:						Omit pennies when preparing this form. Circle "Est" if estimated or "Act" if actual amounts.									
						Est Act		Est Act		Est Act		Est Act		Est Act	
Prepared by	Date														
1	TOTAL SALES	+				$ -									
a	Less charge sales (A/R)	—													
b	Plus cash collected from A/R	+													
1T	NET CASH IN FROM SALES	=	+		-		-		-		-		-		-	
2	CASH OUT FOR GOODS														
a	Purchases for resale	+													
b	Production/store supplies	+													
c	Contract services	+													
d	Packaging/freight	+													
2T	TOTAL CASH OUT FOR GOODS	=	—				-		-		-		-		-	
3	CASH FOR OPERATIONS														
a	Gross wages	+													
b	Payroll taxes-employer share	+													
c	Worker Compensation	+													
d	Accounting, legal, professional	+													
e	Advertising & promotions	+													
f	Auto expenses	+													
g	Bad debts	+													
h	Bank, credit card charges	+													
i	Charitable contributions	+													
j	Insurance	+													
k	Interest expense	+													
l	Miscellaneous	+													
m	Office supplies	+													
n	Rent	+													
o	Repairs & maintenance	+													
p	Taxes & licenses	+													
q	Telephone	+													
r	Trash/waste disposal	+													
s	Utilities	+													
3T	TOTAL CASH OUT FOR OPERATIONS	=	—						-		-		-		-	
4T	NET CASH FROM OPERATIONS		=						-		-		-		-	
5	OTHER CASH IN														
a	Sales tax collected	+													
b	Loan proceeds	+													
c	Add back interest expense	+													
d	Owner contributions	+													
5T	TOTAL OTHER CASH IN	=	+						-		-		-		-	
6	OTHER CASH OUT														
a	Sales tax paid	+													
b	Debt service-principal	+													
c	Capital equipment/vehicle purchases	+													
d	Building & improvements	+													
e	Owner draw (including estimated taxes)	+													
6T	TOTAL OTHER CASH OUT		—						-		-		-		-	
7T	NET CHANGE IN CASH		=						-		-		-		-	
8T	BEGINNING CASH		+						-		-		-		-	
9T	ENDING CASH		=						$ -		$ -		$ -		$ -	

CORE FOUR® Business Planning Course

JUN		JUL		AUG		SEP		OCT		NOV		DEC		TOTALS			
Est	Act	Est	Act	Est	Act	Est	Act	Est	Act	Est	Act	Est	Act				
														$ -		+	1
														-		–	a
														-		+	b
-		-		-		-		-		-		-		-	+	=	1T
																	2
														-		+	a
														-		+	b
														-		+	c
														-		+	d
-		-		-		-		-		-		-		-	–	=	2T
																	3
														-		+	a
														-		+	b
														-		+	c
														-		+	d
														-		+	e
														-		+	f
														-		+	g
														-		+	h
														-		+	i
														-		+	j
														-		+	k
														-		+	l
														-		+	m
														-		+	n
														-		+	o
														-		+	p
														-		+	q
														-		+	r
														-		+	s
-		-		-		-		-		-		-		-	–	=	3T
-		-		-		-		-		-		-		-	=		4T
																	5
														-		+	a
														-		+	b
														-		+	c
														-		+	d
-		-		-		-		-		-		-		-	+	=	5T
																	6
														-		+	a
														-		+	b
														-		+	c
														-		+	d
														-		+	e
-		-		-		-		-		-		-		-	–		6T
-		-		-		-		-		-		-		-	=		7T
-		-		-		-		-		-		-		-	+		8T
$ -	$ -	$ -	$ -	$ -	$ -	$ -	$ -		=		9T

OPERATIONS PLANNING

CONTENTS

OPERATIONS PLANNING INTRODUCTION

PROBLEM

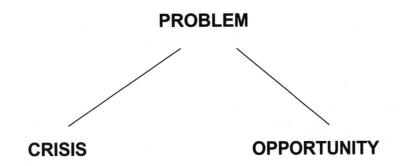

CRISIS

OPPORTUNITY

This section of the CORE FOUR® Business Planning Course is designed to raise your awareness of key issues that your business *must* address in order to be a legitimate, successful business.

> **Not all issues that may impact your business are described in this section. The information presented is not intended to be specific. It is not intended to present the total sum of information that you may need to operate your business in compliance with all laws. Federal and state regulations may change at any time. You must determine what applies to your business.**

This section does, however, identify key issues that, if you are not in compliance or do not address them, *could close your business*. It also helps to set the tone for the attitude you want to develop as a business owner: *an ounce of prevention is worth a pound of cure*.

A PROBLEM – IS IT A CRISIS OR AN OPPORTUNITY?

Avoiding problems usually results in a crisis:

Mary's business was invisible because the city made her take her sign down – it did not comply with local sign ordinances.

John's business was closed by the state Sales Tax Division because he owed $137 in sales taxes and avoided paying them.

Confronting problems creates opportunities for success:

Nancy visited with the city zoning office before purchasing a building for her business. She learned that the building must be brought up to local codes. She did some research and found out that the improvements would cost $25,000 more than her budget. She found another, more appropriate business site.

Laws and regulations govern us all. They are essential for an orderly and successful society.

Operations planning is where you can anticipate and prevent problems and crises by planning to operate a legitimate, professional business.

FORM OF BUSINESS

WHAT DOES FORM OF BUSINESS MEAN?

Form of business describes the legal form of your business. The legal form essentially defines the relationship of the business to its owner or owners and to the public on such matters as:

- The business relationship that owners, partners, officers, or shareholders will have in areas of accountability, responsibility, authority, and distribution of profits.

- The tax impact and reporting requirements of the business.

- The complexity and expense of organizing the business or of ceasing business operations.

Remember, whether you are a sole proprietor or in business with another person as a partnership or corporation, you and your business are *separate economic entities*.

FORMS OF BUSINESS

- Sole proprietorships, most often selected for many startup businesses.

- Partnerships, which include general or limited partnerships.

- Corporations, which, for tax purposes, are identified as either "C" corporations or "S" corporations.

- Some states offer other forms of business including Limited Liability Corporations and Limited Liability Partnerships.

HOW SHOULD YOU CHOOSE?

Consult with *experienced* business, legal, and tax advisors to discuss your business and its goals, and the relationships to the business that you have planned.

Primary considerations are:

- Who will be accountable, responsible and authorized to own and control the business?

- Who will be liable for debts and obligations of the business?

- Who will receive profit distributions and when?

Other considerations include:

What the business does. Is the business a manufacturer? There may be serious product liability risks associated with certain types of manufactured products, such as sporting equipment or children's toys. Products such as dish towels or picture frames may be less vulnerable to product liability issues.

Planned growth of the business. If outside investors will be needed for financing growth, a corporation provides the best structure for raising capital.

The relationships between you and other people involved in the business. *Legally*, partners *share equally* in the *right* and *responsibility* to manage the business, *regardless* of what a partnership agreement may define. Partners also share responsibility for all *debts* and *obligations* of the business, often regardless of what a partnership agreement may define. Many partnerships have failed even though the partners were relatives or long-time friends. The statistics on failed business partnerships may surpass the statistics on failed marriages.

THE PARTNERSHIP TOAST

HERE'S TO YOU, AND HERE'S TO ME
and if we ever disagree,
here's to me!

If you and your partner are trying to make a decision, and you are wrong and your partner is wrong, who's right? In a 50/50 partnership, how do decisions get made when the two partners disagree?

PREPARE A CONFLICT RESOLUTION PLAN

A conflict resolution plan generally involves the intervention of a *third party* on whom both partners *agree*. If a conflict arises that cannot be resolved, the third party is authorized to make decisions reflecting the best interests of the business, not the partners.

The conflict resolution plan merits consideration whether you have a partnership, corporation, or sole proprietorship in which more than one family member or owner has responsibilities or interests.

About 50% of all marriages end in divorce. Over 50% of all partnerships end in "divorce" as well. When a partnership dissolves, the impact on the people involved can be both emotionally and financially devastating and can break lifetime bonds of trust and friendship. If there is a plan in place to handle conflict, then the business, the partnership, and the personal relationships can survive the stresses and strains of disagreement.

The table on the following pages depicts some considerations that may influence your choice of form of business. The table is not complete, and should not be relied upon for all of your decision-making.

Search the web for more information. The following sites may be helpful: **www.legacyassociates.com, www.business.com,** and **www.kentuckymediation.com.**

Consult legal, accounting, tax, and business consulting professionals for their advice and assistance in selecting the most appropriate form of organization for your business.

Forms of Business Chart

Considerations	Sole Proprietorship	Partnership	Corporation
Number of owners	Only one	Two or more	One or more
Complexity and expense of organizing the business	No legal requirements.	Statutory requirements. Consult both tax and legal advisors.	Legal requirements. Consult both tax and legal advisors.
Liability of the business owners	Owner is personally liable for all debts of the business, even if the debts exceed the owner's investment in the business.	Each partner is personally liable for all debts of the business, even if the debts exceed the partner's investment in the business, and even if the partner did not consent to the debt.	The corporation is a separate legal entity and in most cases that entity is liable for all debts of the corporation. Shareholders are *generally* exempt from personal liability beyond their investment in the corporation, but not always.
Distribution of profits and losses	Proprietor receives all profits and takes all losses.	Profits and losses are passed to partners as specified in their partnership agreement.	C-Corp: Profits and losses belong to and may be distributed by the corporation. S-Corp: Profits and losses flow through to shareholders in proportion to their shareholdings.
Management control and decision-making	Sole proprietor has full and complete authority.	All partners share equally in their right and responsibility to manage and control the business regardless of partnership agreement.	Rules for decision-making are established by law but may be modified by articles of incorporation or bylaws.
Financing startup and operation of the business	Limited to the amount the owner has or can personally secure.	Generally limited to the amounts each partner has or can personally secure.	Can raise capital by selling stocks or bonds.
Transferability of ownership	Transfer assets of business to new owner.	Determined by partnership agreement or by law.	Transferred by sale of stock.
Continuity of business after withdrawal or death of owner	Terminates at the death of proprietor or if proprietor is unable to manage business.	Determined by partnership agreement or by statute.	Has no legal effect on business but may impair operation of business without key personnel.
Extent of government regulation	No special regulations other than taxes or hazardous waste-type regulations. The least restrictive, most private form of business.	No special regulations other than taxes or hazardous waste-type regulations, and basic statutory rules for basic partnership management and relationships between partners and third persons.	Generally more formal and complex rules established by state and federal laws...also, most government filings are public documents.
Compensation for services	Not an employee.	Not employees of the business.	Shareholder-employees receive salaries and wages.
Disposition of ownership interest	Proprietor can sell the assets or transfer them after changing the form of the business to a partnership or corporation. Proprietor can close the business and keep the assets.	Sale or exchange of partner's interest is governed by special rules and complex tax laws and is best undertaken with guidance from a tax advisor.	Individual shareholders can sell stock to dispose of their ownership. The corporation can liquidate all or a portion of its assets. Corporate liquidation or closure is governed by special rules and complex tax laws and is best undertaken with guidance from a tax advisor.

Considerations	Sole Proprietorship	Partnership	Corporation
Who is the taxpayer?	Business owner.	Each partner in accordance with his or her share as specified in partnership agreement.	C-Corp: First the corporation, then shareholders who are taxed on dividends they receive. S-Corp: The corporation is not taxed; however, like a partnership, each shareholder is taxed in accordance with his or her ownership.
Unemployment Taxes (FUTA, SUTA)	FUTA: Children under 21, spouse, parent are exempt. SUTA: Children under 18, spouse, parent are exempt.	Owners are exempt.	C-Corp: Pay FUTA and SUTA on owners salary. S-Corp: Pay FUTA and SUTA on owners salary, but generally can't collect.
FICA (Social Security and Medicare)	Children under 18 are exempt; can save about $600 in FICA per child when paying $4000 per child.	Pay FICA on children unless parents are the only partners.	C-Corp and S-Corp: Pay FICA on owners salary.
Income tax impact	The proprietor combines net income or losses from the business with income and losses from other sources of the proprietor, and pays income tax at the proprietor's individual income tax rate, whether or not business income is withdrawn for personal use or retained in the business. Proprietor also pays self-employment tax (SE Tax) on profits. The business entity does not pay income tax.	Each partner combines his or her profits or losses from the business with income and losses* from other sources of the partner, and pays income tax at the partner's individual income tax rate, whether or not the income is withdrawn for personal use or retained in the business. Partners also pay self-employment tax (SE tax) on profits. *Certain deductions may not be permitted, and losses are generally limited to partner's adjusted basis in partnership.	C-Corporations are separate taxable entities, and profits are taxed at current federal tax rates; then (like partnerships) shareholder distributions are taxed at each individual shareholder's income tax rate. S-Corporation profits are not taxed. Similar to partnerships, shareholders are taxed on their share of profits at each individual shareholder's income tax rate. Corporations may also pay a state Corporate (Franchise) Income Tax. Corporations in some states pay a minimum fee, in addition to any tax liability the business may have.
Selection of tax year	Generally uses calendar year.	Generally the same tax year as the principal partners. May establish a fiscal tax year if can demonstrate to IRS that there is a business purpose for a fiscal tax year.	May establish a fiscal tax year that conforms to natural business cycle when first income tax return is filed (unless a personal service corporation which must demonstrate to IRS that there is a business purpose for a fiscal tax year).
What tax forms are used? *See your state income tax guide for state forms*	FED: Form 1040, Individual Income Tax Return; Schedule C or Schedule C-EZ (Farmers Schedule F); and Schedule SE.	FED: Partnership on Form 1065 and Schedules K, K-1 or E. Partner on Form 1040.	FED: Corporation on Form 1120, Form 1120-A or Form 1120S and supporting forms and schedules. Shareholder on Form 1040.

ASSUMED NAME

If you conduct business using a name *other than your own full, true name*, your state may require that you register the business name with your state. This provides information to consumers of the identity of the business owner.

If Sara Angelo operates a business as a sole proprietor with a business name of "Sara Angelo Consulting," she may not need to register an assumed name. If she does business as "Angelo Consulting," she may be required to register the assumed name "Angelo Consulting." Sara Angelo, dba Angelo Consulting, means Sara is doing business as Angelo Consulting.

Registration of an assumed name generally does not guarantee the protection of the use of the business name by other persons, but it may prevent or minimize such use. Once you have registered your business name, the state registration office may inform you each time someone else files a similar name. You can decide whether to take legal action to stop the other person from using the name.

Before you register your business name, you can usually ask your state registration office for a name search. You provide the business name; they will search and advise you if it or similar names exist. If there are similar or identical names, the search operator will advise you and explain your options.

Karen Johnson wanted to name her business "Management Resources." When she checked on a name search, she found there were two businesses with similar names: Management Resources Services, and Resource Management. The search operator advised that one of these businesses was a cleaning service. The search operator also advised that if Karen really wanted to use the words management and resources, she would have to make the business name distinctly unique from the others, such as "Strategic Management Resources," or "Johnson Management Resources." Karen's business was a computer consulting firm. She decided she didn't want to be mistakenly identified with a cleaning service. She re-thought her name choices and selected "Johnson Computer Resources."

There are statutes governing the naming of corporations. It's wise to seek legal advice when naming your corporation.

Remember – the name of your business is often the first contact you have with your marketplace.

A clear, simple business name that conveys what your business does will simplify decision-making for consumers.

HOME-BASED BUSINESSES

For many entrepreneurs, basing a new business in your home can be a good way to get started. There are more than 20 million home-based businesses in America and the number grows each year.

You will need to determine if the needs of your business match the design, needs, and use of your home.

Consider these issues when thinking about doing business from home:

- How will you initiate and maintain contact with customers?
- Do you have the necessary space?
- How much inventory is involved? Do you have ample storage space?
- What equipment do you need? Where will it be kept and used?
- Will you need to remodel to suit business needs?
- Is this a first step toward renting or owning commercial space?
- Will customers expect to reach you at all times? Will that interfere with your family needs? How will you handle it?
- Does having your business in your home present the right image to your customers?
- What problems are presented because your business is in your home?
- Do the advantages outweigh the disadvantages?

If home-based business is for you, remember to carry appropriate insurance coverage. Your homeowner's policy will not provide what you need.

Keep good records of all home-business costs. Including a tax professional prior to establishing your business can be helpful. See also IRS Publication 587, Business Use of Your Home, at www.irs.gov

Be prepared to develop discipline not needed when you have another business location. Maintaining regular hours, accomplishing tasks, and meeting deadlines can be more difficult from the comfort of your home office.

TAX IDENTIFICATION NUMBERS

YOU ARE AUTHORIZED, RESPONSIBLE, AND ACCOUNTABLE TO DETERMINE YOUR BUSINESS RESPONSIBILITIES

The information provided in this section is provided to *guide* you on your own exploration and fact-finding process.

It is critical that you *verify* and *validate* the information you receive about your tax and other legal compliance issues. *Always* go *directly to the taxing authority* to find out what your responsibilities and procedures are. Whenever possible, get the information, instructions or opinions that you need *in writing* from the people *authorized* to give them. A discussion with your brother-in-law, your neighbor, a business counselor, or another business owner about whether or not you are required to collect and pay a specific type of tax won't hold up in court.

The Internal Revenue Service has a web site at **www.irs.gov**. From this site, you can download every required federal tax filing form or publication. If you have the opportunity and access, it's an important site to explore and familiarize yourself with.

Your state may also have a web site for its business tax laws.

Become familiar with how to *access* state, federal and local offices that are responsible for the rules and regulations your business must follow. You are a taxpayer. These are services that are provided because you are a taxpayer and are required to comply, or because you are a citizen and a business owner entitled to the benefits that may be offered.

TAX IDENTIFICATION NUMBERS

A business may be responsible for paying more than one type of federal or state tax. Each taxing authority assigns a different identification number to your business, just as each of your vendors assigns your business a different customer account.

Apply for these required ID numbers as soon as you open your business, or as soon as you *plan* to hire employees. It can take time. Be sure to plan ahead.

When you get these ID numbers, *safeguard them and use them accurately*. Some business owners delegate this task to an accountant or an attorney. You can delegate the task to whomever you wish, but remember – you are accountable, responsible and authorized, *no matter what*. These ID numbers belong to your business, and your business belongs to you. It's important for you to mind your business!

FOUR PRINCIPAL TYPES OF IDENTIFICATION NUMBERS

- State Tax Identification Number
- State Workforce Identification Number
- State Sales and Use Tax Permit
- Federal Employer Identification Number (EIN)

State Tax Identification Number

You may need a state tax identification number if you:

- Have employees.
- Make retail sales.
- Withhold state income taxes from employees.
- Make estimated tax payments.
- File a state income tax return for your business.
- Pay state special taxes such as alcohol, tobacco, or gasoline taxes.
- Are a vendor of goods or services to a state government agency.
- Purchase a business other than a corporation.

Contact your state revenue department to receive copies of the application form and instructions.

Workforce Identification Number

Businesses that have employees may be required to register with their state workforce center to receive an identification number. It may be different than the number you receive from your state revenue department. This number identifies your business as an employer who is required to pay unemployment tax.

Federal Employer Identification Number (EIN)

If you are going to have employees, or if you have any form of business other than a sole proprietorship, the business *must* have a federal employer identification number (EIN).

To apply, contact the Internal Revenue Service. Request form SS-4, Application for Employer Identification Number – you can also download this form from the IRS web site.

You must use your EIN on all tax returns or other documents you send to the IRS. You must also provide your EIN to other persons who use your EIN to report payments to you. If you do not furnish your identification number as required, you will be subject to penalties.

If you purchase an existing business, or your organization or the ownership of business changes, you must apply for a new EIN.

State Sales and Use Tax ID

Check with your state revenue department for sales and use tax identification number requirements or permits before making sales. The permit shows that you are authorized to make retail sales or provide taxable services in the state.

Pay close attention to all of your ID numbers. Keep them current and record them accurately. Sloppy work when reporting information using incorrect ID numbers could result in time-consuming efforts to correct problems, as well as additional taxes, interest, or penalties.

TAXES

ABOUT TAXES

As a business owner you are accountable, authorized, and responsible for complying with tax laws. Even if you hire a tax preparer, you will be responsible for penalties, interest, and tax payments if an error is made on your tax return. You may negotiate reimbursement of penalties and interest with the tax preparer, but the IRS will be paid, no matter what, and you are responsible for payment.

It is your responsibility to have a basic understanding of tax issues in order for you to work effectively with a tax preparer or to do your own taxes.

Taxes are every citizen's responsibility.

To be sure all taxpayers pay their fair share of taxes, the law provides penalties if you do not file returns or pay taxes as required. Criminal penalties may be imposed for willful failure to file, tax evasion, or making a false statement.

Taxes that your business has *withheld* on *behalf of its employees* or *collected as sales tax* are *not dollars that you can use to cash flow your business*. These dollars do not belong to you or to your business. Taxes that your business owes must be paid based on accurate information and timely tax payments.

Your business could be *closed* by a taxing agency if you fail to comply with all tax laws.

If you run a healthy business and pay your taxes, you will have nothing to fear from a taxing authority.

Keeping accurate records, filing accurate tax returns, and paying your taxes in a timely manner are the key to your "tax" peace of mind and prevention of tax hassles and trauma.

There are many avenues of tax sheltering that are legitimate and appropriate for use by all taxpayers. It is illegal and foolish to think that hiding income or creating false expenses is a way to reduce a tax liability. Further, if your business cannot cash flow or be profitable without "cheating" on taxes, it is not a healthy business.

Educate yourself as much as you can about all tax issues related to your business.

Take advantage whenever you can of legitimate tax shelters, deductions and credits.

All taxing agencies are willing to work with business people, especially when a business is being started. They can be part of your business team.

FIVE PRINCIPAL TYPES OF BUSINESS TAXES

⇒ Business Income Tax
⇒ Self-Employment Tax
⇒ Excise Tax
⇒ Employment Taxes
⇒ Sales and Use Taxes

The Internal Revenue Services publishes a general tax calendar each year. You can order this calendar from the IRS or you can download it from the **www.irs.gov** web site. This publication explains when to file returns and make tax payments.

BUSINESS INCOME TAX

Every business must file an annual income tax return. Which form you use and how you pay the tax depends on how your business is organized.

See the table on pages 4-OP – 5-OP in the FORM OF BUSINESS section of this book for the type of return your business is required to file.

SELF-EMPLOYMENT TAX

Self-Employment tax is the Social Security and Medicare tax for *sole proprietors*, self-employed farmers and fishermen, and members of a partnership. You figure self-employment tax on the *profits* from your business using Schedule SE, and report it on your Form 1040.

Self-employment tax is the *same tax paid by you and your employer* for FICA and Medicare when you are an employee. When you are an employee, you and your employer each pay half. When you are self-employed, you pay it *all* – you are both your own employer and your own employee.

EXCISE TAX

If you manufacture or sell certain products, you may have to pay excise taxes. There may also be excise tax on certain kinds of businesses, certain transactions and the use of various kinds of equipment, facilities and products.

EMPLOYMENT TAXES

If you have employees you are required by federal and most state laws to withhold or pay employment taxes on their behalf, including:

- Federal Income Tax Withholding
- Social Security (FICA) and Medicare Taxes
- Federal Unemployment (FUTA) Tax
- State Income Tax Withholding
- State Unemployment Tax

Federal Income Tax Withholding

You, as an employer, must calculate and withhold employee federal income taxes from employee paychecks, and must report on and pay these taxes.

Social Security and Medicare Taxes

An employer must pay one-half of these taxes and must withhold the other half from the employee. The employer is required to pay and report on these taxes. If you are a sole proprietor with no employees, this is called Self-Employment tax.

Federal Unemployment Tax (FUTA)

An employer reports and pays FUTA tax separately from Social Security and Medicare tax and withheld income tax. FUTA tax is paid only from the employer's funds. Employees do not pay this tax.

State Income Tax Withholding

An employer must calculate and withhold the employee state income taxes from the employee paychecks, and must report on and pay these taxes to the state.

State Unemployment Tax

An employer reports and pays unemployment tax separately from Social Security, Medicare and withheld income tax. Unemployment tax is paid only from the employer's funds. Employees do not pay this tax.

SALES AND USE TAXES

In some states, sales tax applies to the gross receipts from selling, leasing or renting tangible items at retail or from providing taxable services in the state.

Use tax is similar to sales tax. Use tax is based on your cost of the taxable purchase and applies when you purchase taxable items to use, store, or consume in your state without paying sales tax.

If you do not make taxable sales but make purchases subject to use tax, you must register to remit use tax.

Some cities have their own sales and use tax. Contact the sales or use tax division in your city.

The sales tax division office can provide information and forms necessary for compliance.

ESTIMATED TAXES

Individuals

Business owners who are proprietors, partners and S-corporation shareholders pay their tax with *estimated tax payments* during the year. This is similar to how your taxes are paid when you are an employee. Based on your annual or hourly earnings, your employer withholds from you and pays to the taxing authority the amount of tax due. Likewise, *estimated taxes* are based on your *annual profits* and are paid by you to the taxing authority. Work with an accountant to determine the amount of your estimated tax payments.

Corporations

A C-corporation must deposit the taxes it owes, including estimated tax payments and any balance due shown on its tax return. Work with an accountant to determine the amount of your estimated tax payments.

DEPOSITING TAX PAYMENTS

You generally must deposit taxes that you owe *before* you file your tax return (just like your employer deposits taxes you owe when you are an employee).

Once you have applied for an Employer Identification Number, you will need to deposit taxes with the IRS. This can be done by mail, by phone, or with electronic withdrawal.

INFORMATION TAX RETURNS

Information returns are required for reporting various kinds of payments made to, or certain payments received from, persons who are *not your employees*. These returns are used to match the payments with each person's income tax return to see if payments were included in income. You must give a copy of each statement you are required to file to the recipient or payer.

Check with your tax accountant to determine if your business is required to file other information returns. Online resources include **www.irs.gov** and your state government website.

IRS Form 1099 is the most commonly used form, similar to a W2 form an employer uses to report wages paid to employees.

If you are a private contractor, your customers should provide you with this form when they pay you more than $600 (this amount may change if the law changes) in one year. If you are an independent contractor who is paid less than $600 in one year by a customer who does not provide the form, *you must still report those amounts as income!*

Your business may be required to file other information returns such as IRS Form 8300, on which cash payments over $10,000 or foreign currency in one or more related business transactions must be reported.

LICENSES AND PERMITS

In many states you may be required to secure one or more business, occupational, or environmental licenses or permits to operate your business for the following reasons:

- To ensure the competency of practitioners.
- To ensure safety and effectiveness of a product or process.
- To prevent fraud or ensure the financial solvency of parties to a business transaction.
- To control access to markets.
- To regulate activities in pursuit of broad social goals like clean air or water.
- To ensure appropriate and responsible use of natural resources.
- To authorize a business to serve as the state's agent for collection of revenue.

Check with your government licensing offices or similar departments to determine which licenses and/or permits your business will need.

www.okcommerce.gov

ZONING

States, counties, cities and townships each have their own unique zoning concerns. These concerns may cover the type of signs your business can display, restrictions or requirements on building construction and improvements, traffic flow, hours of business activity, or land use restrictions.

You may be required to apply for a *land use permit* or special variance, or may be required to comply with restrictions and inspections of your business property *prior to its use for business.*

Check with your township, city, and county planning and zoning office to find out about specific requirements. Check with your city engineering office or other local officials as well.

POLLUTION CONTROL PROGRAMS

Laws concerning waste disposal are becoming more restrictive each year. Your state Pollution Control Agency is responsible for administering your state pollution control programs. These programs address air and water quality, and hazardous and solid waste.

You may be surprised to find out what the costs of disposal are for what you might think is routine trash. You may also be surprised to find out what wastes are considered hazardous. Most importantly, you may be astonished to find out what the penalties are for non-compliance.

If you have any concerns about your business, the process, or products you produce or sell, contact your state Pollution Control Agency to learn about restrictions you may be required to comply with. Don't make assumptions that your waste products are routine. Did you know that that cooking oil from restaurants is considered toxic waste, and that there are laws governing the disposal of cooking oil by commercial businesses?

Also check with your local landfill or recycling centers to identify your projected trash disposal costs. These costs will be based on the types and quantities of trash your business generates.

ISSUES FOR EMPLOYERS

It is very important for you to understand the employer/employee relationship because:

- As an employer *you* will be accountable and responsible for payroll tax withholding and deposits of payroll taxes.

- If you are an independent contractor or if you hire one, you will want to clearly define your relationship with your customer.

Errors in judgment about a relationship your business may have with an independent contractor, or if you are an independent contractor, can result in time consuming and costly problem resolution. See IRS Publication 15A for more details on employer/contractor relationships.

TYPES OF EMPLOYMENT RELATIONSHIPS

Common law employee rules include several factors to determine whether an employer-employee relationship exists. They include, *but are not limited to:*

- Control: Does the employer have the right to control the manner and means of performing the work?
- Mode of payment: How is the worker paid – on a regular basis, hourly, bi-weekly, or by flat fee for the job?
- Does the employer withhold taxes and provide benefits?
- Materials and tools: Does the employee provide his or her own tools?
- Control of the premises: Does the hiring entity own or control the premises where the work is performed?
- Right of discharge: Does the employer have the ability to discharge the worker?
- Profit or Loss: Can the employee/contractor make a profit or risk a loss?

None of these factors alone will determine whether an employment relationship exists. The most important factor is the hiring entity's right to control the manner and means of the work.

A worker may not be an employee under common law rules, but may be a statutory employee for certain purposes including payment or withholding of FICA, federal and state unemployment compensation taxes, fair labor standards act compliance, and occupational safety and health requirements. A federal or state statute may exempt certain employers or employees from its application.

People who follow an independent trade, business or profession offering their services to the general public are usually considered independent contractors. In general, the individual will be considered an independent contractor if the business entity obtaining the person's services has the legal right to control the result of the work, but does not have the legal right to control the manner and means of accomplishing the result.

Both state and federal statutes may define employees covered by their own laws. See IRS Publication 937 and Publication 15A. They include discussions on whether an individual is an employee. Contact both federal and state sources to determine the employment relationship.

Treat your employees how you would like to be treated as an employee!

OTHER EMPLOYMENT ISSUES

Minimum Wage Requirements

Federal law requires a minimum wage per hour for workers. Some employees are excluded under narrowly defined specific exemptions provided in law. Employers should check with the U.S. Department of Labor and Industry at **www.dol.gov/esa/whd.**

Your state may have additional minimum wage requirements. Check with your state labor department.

Some communities have "Living Wage" ordinances that require specified wage minimums. Check with your city offices.

Overtime Pay Requirements

Federal law requires overtime pay at a specified rate under a variety of conditions. Overtime requirements may vary in different industries.

Your state may require different overtime pay strategies.

For more information contact the U.S. Department of Labor and your state labor department at **www.dol.gov/esa/whd.**

Workers' Compensation

Workers' Compensation is insurance. Workers' Compensation provides compensation to employees who have a work-related injury or disease. Compensation may include partial wage replacement and full payment of medical and rehabilitation costs.

Generally, all employers are required to have Workers' Compensation insurance and display the name of their carrier in a conspicuous place.

You can contact your insurance company or your state labor department – Workers' Compensation Division, for information on this insurance. Contact several providers of Workers' Compensation to determine the lowest cost. All policies provide coverage mandated by law; only prices vary. Other factors to consider may include claims servicing, safety counseling, and the carrier's reputation.

[handwritten note in left margin: State of OK. can exempt owner from paying w.c.]

Occupational Safety And Health (OSHA)

OSHA applies to all places of employment in your state with the exception of those covered exclusively by the federal government. Find information at **www.osha.gov**.

Contact the Occupational Safety and Health Division of your state labor department to learn about your state Occupational Safety and Health (OSHA) issues and requirements.

Other Considerations

Learn more about what your choices and responsibilities will be concerning:

American's with Disabilities Act (ADA)
Child Labor Laws
Citizenship and immigrant status
Jury duty
Independent contractors (you hiring them)
Independent contractor (you being hired as one)
Holidays – paid or unpaid
Military Leave
Vacations – paid or unpaid
Family Leave Act

Employee Manual

You can make it easy for employees to be aware of your policies by collecting and binding them in an employee manual. Making government regulations and other pertinent rules available in one place can clarify situations for both employees and employer.

Numerous resources exist to assist you with employee manuals. Check with your state's departments of trade, economic development, and labor. Several federal websites may be of help when writing your manual. One is **www.eeoc.gov**. Use the section on quick start for employees.

MANAGING RISK

INSURANCE

Insurance is purchased from an agent or broker. An agent represents one insurance company and offers only that company's insurance lines. A broker may represent several insurance companies and may offer a wider range of coverage.

Competence of the agent or broker is important. Before selecting your agent or broker, ask other business owners for references. Ask them about the type of insurance they carry. Are they satisfied with claim resolutions? Are their insurance costs reasonable? Was their agent helpful with any claim issues? Were they comfortable discussing insurance issues with their agent? Was their agent willing to explain everything carefully?

The insurance company or carrier should also be a healthy business. Is the company stable? Are they rated? Check with the your state Insurance Commission for information on the financial condition of the insurance company or visit **www.ambest.com**. There is also a book at the most public libraries called A.M. Best Insurance Company Ratings.

CAUTION: Don't buy based only on the cheapest price. If you don't feel comfortable with your agent, or if the insurance company is a fly-by-night or poorly rated company, price won't make a difference when you have a claim.

Considerations

If your office is in your home, your homeowners or renters insurance does not cover business equipment, inventory or supplies. You may be able to add a special business endorsement to your homeowner or renter policy.

Elect replacement value on any property or equipment. Without this election, you may not receive enough money to replace a damaged or stolen item. Without replacement coverage, you will be paid for the current depreciated value, usually a much lower amount than replacement cost.

Record all of your insured property in writing and with photographs and/or videotapes. Also, keep copies of all receipts for insured property. Make two copies and keep lists and photos at separate locations or in a safety deposit box.

Ask about "Standard" or "Umbrella" policies. Some insurance companies offer these for different types of businesses. These policies can provide substantially more coverage for modest increases in premiums.

Paying insurance premiums once a year can use more cash than your business can afford. Ask about monthly, quarterly or semi-annual payments. There may be a small charge for this service, but cash flow is your focus.

TYPES OF INSURANCE

General Liability

Provides coverage for claims of property damage or personal injury resulting from general business operations. Example: a customer trips on your entry step and injures his back. Your insurance should have coverage limits for this type of situation.

Product Liability

Protects against claims of injuries or damages related to defects of products produced or sold by your business. Expensive and time-consuming to defend against.

Property Damage

Protects business property in the event of fires, vandalism, windstorms, hail, lightning, etc.

Coverage is also available to cover glass storefronts, inventory, machinery and equipment, records, personal property of employees, etc. Check for additional coverage for flood insurance, if needed.

Workers' Compensation

Required if you have employees! Provides payment of compensation benefits to injured employees of a business. Compensation may include partial wage replacement and payment of medical and rehabilitation costs.

Health and Medical

Provides coverage for medical expenses. High medical costs can bankrupt a business owner. Determine if this is a benefit you can afford for you and your employees.

Federal and some state laws require that if the business pays for health insurance for the owner, it must pay for employees. If the business can afford health coverage for you and your family, you may take an owner draw to cover the amount of insurance. Be sure to pay your personal health insurance with your *personal* income by writing a *personal* check.

Disability or Long-Term Income Continuance

Provides income replacement for you if you are unable to work due to illness or injury.

Key Person or Life Insurance

Provides coverage in case of disability or death of the business owner or key person in the business. You are typically the key person.

Business Interruption

Provides coverage if business activity is stopped by unforeseen event. Covers lost income and extra expenses caused by the event. Usually defines income as the difference between normal income and actual income earned during the interruption.

BONDING

Your business may be required by statute to be bonded, or it may be more desirable for your customers if you are bonded. If you are required to be licensed to do business in your state, check with your licensing authority and to determine if bonding is needed.

A bond is a contract similar to an insurance policy. It provides protection for the consumer against financial loss caused by an act or default of your business.

- Surety bonds guarantee performance assumed by a contract or imposed by law.

- Fidelity bonds guarantee against loss due to dishonesty of employees.

To find a bonding company, ask another business owner for a referral, talk with your insurance agent for referrals, or check your phone book for bonding companies.

MANAGING INSURANCE COSTS

Insurance prices from different agencies and different providers change over time. Each year, you should review your insurance coverage to be sure the amount of coverage is adequate based on your business growth, and compare prices to assure that you are getting the best value. Insurance costs are an expensive commitment by a business, and it is wise to manage these costs effectively.

The insurance worksheet on the following page will assist you in tracking separate insurance quotes.

Discussion Items:

What is the difference between current cost and replacement cost?

What amount should you have for deductible?

INSURANCE WORKSHEET

Type of Coverage	Quote #1		Quote #2	
Date:				
Insurance Company:				
Agent or Broker:				
Type of Coverage	Amount	Cost	Amount	Cost
GENERAL LIABILITY				
Bodily injury to others				
Key person				
Business interruption				
Extra expenses after loss				
Other				
Total Premium				
Terms				
PREMISES				
Replacement cost				
Structure				
Fire				
Windstorm				
Lightning				
Vandalism				
Glass damage				
Signage				
Other				
Total Premium				
Terms				
EQUIPMENT AND INVENTORY				
Fixtures and equipment				
Automobile				
Equipment and machinery				
Inventory				
Records				
Robbery and burglary				
Other				
Total Premium				
Terms				
OTHER				
Income continuation				
Life insurance/Key person				
Total Premium				

CORE FOUR® Business Planning Course

LEGAL AND ACCOUNTING PROFESSIONALS

Many business owners work with accountants for financial statement preparation, financial analysis, and preparing income taxes.

Attorneys may be consulted to help prepare partnership agreements, contracts, filing incorporation papers or with other legal matters.

HOW TO FIND AN ACCOUNTANT OR ATTORNEY

Compile a list of recommended service providers. Do you know other business owners who have accountants or attorneys? Are they satisfied with the services they pay for? When asking people for references, also ask what types of services are provided, whether or not they are comfortable asking questions of their accountant or attorney, and whether or not they get satisfactory answers. If your referral sources are intimidated by their accountant or attorney, ask them why.

Once you have a list of recommended providers, pick up your phone and call them!

Explain that you are a new business owner and you are shopping for accounting or legal service providers. Refer (if you have permission) to the person who suggested their name to you. Be prepared to ask specific questions. Try to set up an appointment for a preliminary (no charge) meeting. Have a list of written questions and concerns, which may include the following:

- Do you work with small startup businesses?
- Could I contact some of your clients?
- What area is your specialty?
- How long have you been practicing?
- What is your fee structure and credit policy?
- Do you encourage your clients to call you with questions, or do you prefer to meet?
- Do you charge for telephone questions?
- What do you expect from your clients?
- What experience do you have working with businesses like mine?
- Will you be working with me or will you assign my work to someone else on your staff?

Your research and interviews will help you determine whether you are comfortable with the accountant or attorney. Did you get your questions answered? Do you feel you will work well with this person? An accountant or attorney can provide valuable services and be a part of your business "team." Selecting an accountant or attorney that is a good fit with you and your business can save you time and headaches in the future.

TIP: Negotiating a fixed fee for a specific service during your startup may be in your best interests.

BANKING

YOUR BUSINESS BANK ACCOUNT

The Internal Revenue Service requires that you *must* have a separate checking account for your business. Remember, you and your business are separate economic entities!

HOW TO SHOP FOR MONEY

An existing relationship is very important when choosing your bank. If you already know your banker, this is a good place to start. However, some banks or credit unions may not offer the range of services your business may need. Think about services your business may need and try to match these with what the bank offers. Convenience is also a factor. Compare several banks in your search.

Prior relationship – If you have a relationship with your banker, it may be appropriate to continue to develop the relationship rather than start from scratch.

Small business orientation – Is the bank "small business friendly?" Does the bank appear knowledgeable about and sympathetic toward small business concerns? Does the bank promote its services to small businesses?

Fees – Most banks charge fees for their services. These fees can cover each check written or deposited, monthly services, and fees for checks written or deposited that are non-sufficient funds checks.

Interest – Does the bank pay interest on your checking account balance?

Minimum deposit – The bank may require that you carry a specific amount of cash on balance at all times, and will charge a higher fee if you do not.

Free services – Some banks still offer free services such as pre-printed checks, endorsement stamps or safe deposit boxes.

LOANS AND CREDIT LINE

The best time to establish a relationship with a banker is when you don't need a loan! Involve your banker in your business *before* you need a loan! Help your banker learn about you and your business. Ask the banker *before* you need a loan what the bank's lending requirements are. Help

your banker help you. Ask what commercial loan products are available. Determine if they suit your business needs.

MERCHANT STATUS

This service provides authorization to accept credit cards. If you are considering accepting credit card charges from your customers, be sure the company you choose has the ability to offer merchant status. There is a cost to providing this service. Research these costs to determine what fits your needs.

OPENING YOUR ACCOUNT

Always check with the bank you have chosen to ask what they require for opening an account. They may require copies of the following:

- Certificate of Assumed Name
- Certificate of Incorporation
- Driver's License Number
- Federal Identification Number

TIP: When ordering business checks, think carefully – they can be very expensive. Consider your record keeping system and whether or not you will benefit from the type of checks offered. Do you need duplicate copies? Stubs? There are many sources for check printing that may be much less expensive sources than the bank.

TYPES OF FUNDING SOURCES

There are many different sources of financing that may be available to your business:
- economic development funds, private and public
- banks
- select credit unions
- equity and angel investors
- lenders through the Small Business Administration (see **www.sba.gov**).

RECORD KEEPING, BOOKKEEPING, & ACCOUNTING

Keeping current and accurate records is essential for your business and is required by federal law.

Your financial reports are what inform you of the results of your business decisions. Without current and accurate financial information, you will not have the most critical information tool that you need to operate your business successfully.

All businesses must have record keeping systems and methods in place; develop these systems and methods *before* you start doing business. Unless you are an accountant or have an accounting background and experience, it will also be important that you:

- Take a fundamental accounting class, and

- Work with an accounting or business consulting professional to develop your record keeping system.

Remember, *you* are the person who is *accountable, authorized and responsible* for everything in your business. Your knowledge of the transactions of your business, and your ability to process them quickly and effectively, will give you a major edge in your ability to manage your business. Even if you hire or contract with someone to do this work, you must have fundamental, working knowledge of how the information is processed.

TWO FUNDAMENTAL RULES OF BOOKKEEPING

The business of doing business takes place one transaction at a time. The fundamental rules are:

- Record each transaction at cost, when it occurs, at the lowest level of detail.

- At the end of each day, process the detail records to the highest level that you can – totals of sales, cash received, and other transaction totals.

If you invest an hour or so of your time at the end of each day, you will save yourself days of time at the end of each month, and you will be very aware of what is happening in your business!

Record keeping is not an option, and if you commit to developing a practical and simple strategy, you will easily incorporate this activity into the daily routine of your business.

COMPUTERIZED ACCOUNTING SYSTEMS

Using a computer to process accounting information requires a serious commitment on behalf of the business owner. Many small businesses can operate effectively with a manual accounting system, or with cash registers that tabulate transactions during each day. In a new, small business, that's a good place to start.

A *person* must record transactions such as sales and bank deposits when they occur. A *person* must also input this data into a computer in order to generate financial reports. Computers don't "do" anything – they merely process information to a higher level, such as for financial statements or income tax returns.

WHY WE KEEP RECORDS

FOR MANAGEMENT

Do I have the information I need to make decisions?

What are the resources of the business?
What debts does the business owe?
Does the business have cash? Earnings? How much? If not, why?
Are expenses too large in relation to sales?
Are amounts owed by customers being collected rapidly?
Are amounts owed by the business being paid on time?
Will the business be able to meet its own debts?
Should an item be discontinued? Added?
What are the trends?
Should selling prices be increased? Decreased?
Can we afford to purchase equipment? Hire someone?

Do I have the data required by my franchise?

FOR LENDERS/CREDITORS

Are the earning prospects good?
What is the debt-paying ability?
Has the business paid debts promptly in the past?
Is collateral sufficient for a loan?
Should credit be granted?

FOR GOVERNMENT

Tax reporting and tax collections.
Compliance with labor laws.

FOR LABOR UNIONS

Labor negotiations and wage agreements.

FOR INVESTORS

For investment decisions.

THINGS YOUR RECORD KEEPING SYSTEM SHOULD HELP YOU KNOW, DO, OR MONITOR

Daily

- Cash on hand, including petty cash.
- Bank balances of all bank accounts (including checking, savings and debt).
- Daily sales totals.
- Daily cash receipts totals.
- All errors in records are identified and corrected.
- A record is maintained of all cash paid out, by cash or by check.
- Daily cash and sales, and charges and cash received, are reconciled.
- Bank deposit is made.
- No cash is disbursed or purchases made without your authorization.
- The hours your employees worked, were sick, or took vacations or other time off.
- Inventory transactions (receipts and sales) are properly recorded.

Weekly

- Accounts receivable balances - take action on all past due from customers.
- Accounts payable balances - stay current with your vendors, take advantage of discounts when cash flow allows.
- Payroll records - be certain all records include current names, addresses, Social Security numbers, number of exemptions, pay period end date, hours worked, pay rate, total wages, deductions, net pay and check number.
- Tax reports and deposits are made (sales tax, withholding taxes, estimated self-employment taxes).
- Required benefits are paid (unemployment compensation, worker's compensation).

Monthly

- Total accounts receivable at end of month and aging (30, 60, 90 days past due).
- Take action to collect bad and slow accounts.
- Total accounts payable at end of month.
- Take action to work with your vendors if you can't pay on time.
- All journal entries are classified and summarized or reconciled. If you find errors, fix them.
- All bank statements are reconciled. If you and the bank statement disagree, work with the bank to solve the problem.
- Petty cash is reconciled.
- All tax deposits are made.
- A profit and loss statement for the month is prepared on a timely basis.
- If your profits are low or you have losses, take action (adjust prices, reduce overhead, prevent pilferage).
- Take inventory.
- Review your inventory to remove slow moving stock and increase inventory of what moves quickly.
- Update your cash flow projections.
- Always use the past and present to make decisions about the future.

AUDIT TRAIL

Record Each Transaction When It Occurs⇒	Summarize Similar Transactions⇒	Report, Analyze, Plan
Input	Process	Output
FACTS	SUMMARIZED FACTS	PRESENTATIONS AND INTERPRETATIONS OF FACTS
Sales Tickets	Sales Journal	
Cash Register Detail	Sales/Cash Receipts Journal	
Customer Invoices	Sales Journal Accounts Receivable Subledger	**Historical Reporting:**
Bank Deposits and Automatic Deposits	Cash Receipts Journal	*Income Tax Returns*
Cash Receipt Slips	Accounts Receivable Subledger	*Financial Statements*
Purchase Orders	Purchases Journal	*Income Statement*
Business Credit Card Transactions		*Balance Sheet*
Receiving Reports and Packing Lists	Inventory Subledger	*Sources/Uses*
Vendor Invoices	Accounts Payable Subledger	*Compliance Reports*
Petty Cash Slips	Cash Disbursements Journal	*Payroll Tax Returns*
Bank Fees	Cash Disbursements Journal	*Other Compliance Reports*
Checks Written	Check Register	
ATM Transactions and Automatic Payments	Accounts Payable Subledger	**Analysis:**
W-4 Forms	Payroll and Payroll Journal	*Ratios*
Time Cards/Records	Payroll and Payroll Journal	*Profitability*
Payroll Checks	Cash Disbursements and Payroll Journal	*PLANNING* *Rolling Cash Flow Projection*
⇓ **Retain the Written Record**	⇓ **Reconcile and Verify All Totals**	

⇓
MONITOR, REVIEW, ANALYZE, COMPARE, PLAN

PURCHASING

For retail or manufacturing businesses, purchasing dollars will be a major use of your cash. Purchasing at the right price, at the right time and in the right quantity is a skill you can develop.

Business owners sometimes make the mistake of buying large quantities to get the lowest prices. This often consumes cash the business needs for operations.

WHAT SHOULD YOU CONSIDER?

- **Terms.** Being able to purchase on terms (credit) is one way to have the products you need. Paying a higher price for products with terms is a good alternative to not having inventory to sell. This way you sell the products and have the money to pay the invoice when it is due. Ask your vendors if they offer terms. Negotiate, if you can, for the longest payment period (60 instead of 30 days).

- **Delivery time and cost of freight**. How long will it take to receive the products? Paying the lowest price and waiting weeks for delivery can be a very costly practice. Consider the type of freight you are paying for and consider different modes of transportation.

- **Order quantities.** Price breaks are offered on quantity purchasing. Buying the right quantity for your business makes sense. Buying more than you need at the lowest price consumes cash, the fuel of your business.

- **Quality.** Is quality important to your customers? You want to purchase products that meet your customers' standards of quality. Don't underestimate what your customers want.

- **Vendor reputation.** Is the company you are ordering from stable? Do they keep their promises? Ask other business owners for recommendations of vendors. You can also consult the Thomas Registry of American Manufacturers (**www.thomasregister.com**) or the U.S. Industrial Directory, both available at most libraries.

- **Bids.** Obtain bids from a number of suppliers. Call or write for bids. Be sure to get bids on the same quantities and qualities. Compare the results. Decide what is most important -- price, delivery time, terms, quality.

NEGOTIATING

Many vendors are open to negotiation. It does not cost you money to ask whether you are receiving the best deal. Remember, you are dealing with another business and they have the same concern as you do – their bottom line. Do your homework and be willing to compromise on some items that are less important to your business. Can you wait for delivery if the price is lower?

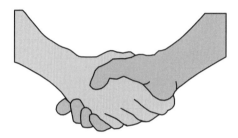

Ask about freight prices. Who pays the freight? Is the vendor willing to pay the freight or split the cost?

Always ask for what you want and then let the vendor respond. Many business owners ask vendors once for better deals and are turned down. The vendor may be open to negotiation after you have established yourself, so ask periodically about discounts. It is easier to negotiate with people they know and have done business with in the past.

KEEP YOUR PROMISES

Honor the commitments you make to your vendors. If you agree to pay by a certain date, pay by that date. Your vendor is counting on your money for operations just like you depend on your customers' money.

Continue to search for vendors and products that meet your customers' needs. Many times business owners stop looking for better deals. They consider it easier to deal with vendors they are comfortable with. That comfort can be costly. Your business is depending on you and your ability to add to your bottom line.

GOALS, FUNCTIONS, POLICIES & PROCEDURES

GOALS

Goals are what the business wants to accomplish. Goals can identify market share or sales levels to be achieved, plans for expansion, plans to purchase capital equipment, plans to hire employees, or any other achievements for the business. Goals are usually defined during the business planning stage, and achievement of goals is measured and monitored during operation of the business. Goals can be re-defined or new goals can be established at any time during the operation of the business.

FUNCTIONS

Functions define areas of responsibility for work to be accomplished. For people who are sole proprietors and who do all of the work of the business, functions describe the various "hats" they will wear when they operate their own business. For businesses with employees, functions describe the "hats" employees will wear. Function descriptions include:

- The area of responsibility, such as finance, sales, purchasing, or manufacturing.
- Who is accountable.
- Who is authorized to make decisions.
- Who is responsible for either doing the work or getting the work done.

POLICIES & PROCEDURES

Policies are the rules and guidelines that the business owner develops which will govern decision-making. Developing a policy manual, like an employee manual, is a method of keeping related materials in one place.

Procedures are instructions that describe how work should be performed. They may include who, what, when, where, and how the work should be done.

SO WHAT?

Why, if you do everything yourself, should you think of your business in this way?

1. You will be extremely busy. It's often tough to pay attention to everything that needs to be done.

2. You may not enjoy each and every facet of what needs to be done in your business. In fact, you may dread and despise certain activities. By defining goals, functions, policies and procedures, you are providing a strategy for yourself that will help you overcome boredom, fear, frustration and anxiety about things you don't want to do.

3. As your business grows, if you pay attention to your goals and policies, they will help you stay on track. By defining procedures you will be readily able to turn work over to employees.

4. In family-owned businesses, this effort at good structure will assure that the business will receive the energy and effort it needs. Many arguments over business issues can be prevented when everyone is clearly aware of what needs to be done, who is responsible, and how work should be done.

5. Some work in the business, such as payroll tax returns, is done quarterly or less often. Without written procedures, it's easy to forget what to do and how to do it.

AN EXAMPLE OF HOW THEY ALL FIT TOGETHER

Goal: To manage the credit relationship we have with our customers to assure timely cash flow.

Function: Credit and Collections Manager.

Who: Nancy Carter, Owner.

Policies:

- All new customer accounts are subject to credit approval by the credit manager.

- All new accounts are limited to a maximum $500 account balance for their first year.

- Any account with a past due balance of greater than 60 days cannot receive additional credit until the account is paid in full.

- Any account due that is older than 90 days will be turned over to a collection agency.

- Any customer that charges over $2,500 per year will receive a $25.00 gift certificate.

- All gift certificates should expire 90 days from date of issue and should be mailed by January 31 each year.

Procedures: *These policies identify that there is some work to be done to comply with the policies. What work should be done? How should the credit manager approve a new account? What does "approval" mean? How can accounts be monitored to assure that new customers do not exceed the $500 credit limit or that a customer with a past-due balance of greater than sixty days does not charge additional purchases? How can you determine which customers should receive a gift certificate?*

Some procedures might include the following (actual procedures would contain step-by-step details):

- Record all customer charges and payments at the *time of sale* on the accounts receivable subsidiary ledger card.

- Compute all account balances at the end of each day.

- Yellow tag any account with a $500 balance or more; apply the tag to the top right of the card.

- Pink tag any account with a past-due balance of greater than sixty days; pink tags should be applied to the top left of the card.

CUSTOMER SERVICE

The main ingredients for your successful business will be your *customers*.

No matter how hard you work or what amount of money you spend, your business will not fulfill your dreams unless you focus on your customers.

People who understand this look at their businesses from their customers' point of view. Ask yourself questions about your products, services, and business practices from your customers' perspectives. Do you like what you see? Do your customers like what they see?

How often do you tell the businesses you shop at that you really appreciate them and are very satisfied with their business?

How often do you tell your friends, family, and others when you are *not satisfied* with a business that you were dealing with?

Typically, you may tell 3 to 4 people when you are satisfied and 16 to 20 people when you are not!

Good customer service can put word-of-mouth advertising to work for your business. Bad customer service can put you out of business.

DEFINING CUSTOMER SERVICE

Customer service is doing whatever it takes to satisfy your customer, within reason of course.

Every contact you have with a customer can be an opportunity to provide excellent customer service. Customer service is a hallmark of small businesses.

You are the person responsible for "getting everything done." In the rush of things it may be easy to treat your customers as interruptions to the important work you are doing. Take every opportunity to provide excellent customer service. Here are some opportunities to shine in the customer service area:

Walk-ins

Always greet your customers with a welcoming smile. Let them know you are happy to see them and have them in your business. Ask how you can help. Pay attention to whether your customer wants your help now or would rather browse first. Let your customers browse, but look to see if they need you. If you are busy with one customer, acknowledge a waiting customer with a nod or a wave. Let them know, if you can, when you will be with them. If it will be a long wait, let them know. Excellent customer service means understanding and acting on the information your customers give you.

Telephone Etiquette

Always answer your business phone in a business-like way. Don't say, "Hello," say "Good morning, ABC Company. How can I help you?" or identify yourself by saying "ABC Company, Rhonda speaking." This is especially important if your business is in your home. Be sure to teach your children to answer the phone in a business-like manner. This call is often the first contact and first impression your customer has with your business. Make it a *great* contact. Smile when you answer the phone, it will make you sound friendlier. Listen to everything your customer has to say before your speak. Ask questions to make certain you understand the customer request. Convey the message that your caller is important to you and your business. When hiring employees who will meet customers, determine their ability and train them to well-represent your business.

Requests for Information

If someone calls and asks for a sample, a catalog, or information, turn this request into an opportunity for excellent customer service. Send the information out the same day you receive the request.

Complaints

Try to determine what the customer is concerned about. If your customer is angry, *let them speak without interrupting*. Never react with anger or defensiveness. Stay focused on the problem. Acknowledge the problem. Rephrase the complaint in your own words so your customer is sure you understand: "You said the toaster didn't pop up when the toast was done?" Don't deny that there is a problem; don't minimize the problem. Always apologize for your customers' *inconvenience* (even if they are wrong!). The one question you can ask that will diffuse nearly any customer complaint is,

"What can I do to make it right for you?"

You will be surprised at how often "making it right" is very easy to accomplish. Once you have taken responsibility for solving the problem, act on the solution. Often, it is problem solving that turns angry or occasional customers into loyal customers.

Repairs and Service

There is an old saying that says, "If you sell it, service it!" If you are not able to service the product, be sure you can tell your customer where, who, and how the product can be serviced. Ask your customer to let you know if they are having problems with the service or repair. Let your customer know you will help in any way you can.

TECHNOLOGY

"New technology" is a buzz word of the 21st century. As a business owner, it is important for you to consider what "new technology" means to you and your business.

CELL PHONES AND PAGERS

Communication is important to your business. How you communicate with customers and vendors may be a lifeline of your business. Traveling salespeople were probably among the first to understand the value of communication on the road. Cell phones and pagers provide the option of directing a salesperson to a new prospect in a timely fashion or having a delivery person make a stop while currently in the area of a calling customer. As the owner of a one-person business, you won't miss important calls or a possible sale while performing the duties of your business if you carry a cell phone or a pager. Be sure that your business needs this added expense.

COMPUTERS

To stay current and up-to-date with your business decisions, transactions, and record keeping, consider how you and your business may use a computer.

Inventory can be tracked on a computer in the very simplest forms, or by using software known as "Point of Sale" (POS). Check with your vendors or industry to see if there is POS software available for your product or service. POS tracks sales at your cash register, simplifies and monitors inventory, and makes a number of orders available to you when your vendor calls.

As stated in the Market Planning section of CORE FOUR®, the 80/20 rule of marketing is that 80% of your sales are made to 20% of your customers. A database of customer information may help you track that 20% of customers. How often do they visit your store? What kinds of products do they buy from you? A simple customer list of names and addresses used to mail out flyers would

begin to build a customer retention program, and the 20% of your big spenders.

Who will do your record keeping? Record keeping is the report card of how well your business is doing. Any level of record keeping can be done on a computer and then electronically transferred to your tax person or accountant. Consider what kind of software your tax person or accountant uses before you purchase, if you decide to computerize your record keeping.

E-MAIL AND INTERNET

Both e-mail and the Internet can be used for communication. They can be used for ordering or taking orders. The Internet can be used for research of new products, new processes, or new markets. E-mail and e-newsletters are a very cost-effective advertising medium.

COMPUTER-ENHANCED EQUIPMENT

Computer-enhanced equipment is found in many industries. Examples include computer-enhanced lathes or saws, road construction equipment, quilting and sewing machines, and most cars. Considerations the business owner has in deciding to use computer-enhanced equipment include quality of product, market niche, production cost savings, or production time. An example of the latter is a well-drilling company that, with new equipment, went from drilling one well every three days to one well per day. This was accomplished by equipping the rig with new technology and becoming computer-enhanced. (Note: this would have increased their sales by 300%; however, the owner chose to increase sales by 200% and vacation in January and February.)

Use of technology continues to play a larger role in all of our lives. A little bit of thought and research about new technology for your business may set you above the competition and ensure long-term success.

BUSINESS DRESS REHEARSAL

You've completed your business plan. You've arranged your business site. You have all of your forms, systems, and equipment. Your helpers are ready.

Consider a business dress rehearsal, where you conduct business with a select group of invited guests. This will allow you to work out any kinks or bugs in your methods – like the retail store that opened to 200 waiting customers and discovered at the first sale that they forgot to get a cash register.

Two primary components of a dress rehearsal are:

1. Presenting your products or services in the environment that most represents how you will do business.

2. Getting feedback from your customers.

Feedback is essential in order for you to evaluate your effectiveness and efficiency.

Many people invite their vendors, lenders, legal and tax providers, and others who have an interest in seeing their business succeed.

For service businesses, a dress rehearsal could consist of volunteering or "testing" your services for a discounted fee to a small, select group of your customers.

For manufacturing businesses, the dress rehearsal is an ongoing part of their startup phase, where methods, techniques, equipment, and technology issues are ironed out.

Customer service is one area where the small business can really be outstanding. You have closer contact with your customers than most large businesses have. Talk to your customers and determine what they want and how you can provide it. Your customers will become loyal customers of your business if you make great customer service your priority!

OPERATIONS PLANNING CHECKLIST

Description	To Do or N/A	Done	Comments
GET READY!			
Select Form of Business			
File Certificate of Assumed Name			
Apply for State Tax Identification Number			
Apply for Federal Tax Identification Number			
Apply for Sales and Use Tax Permit			
Determine tax filing requirements for business			
Determine tax filing requirements as employer			
Determine tax filing requirements for Self-Employment Tax			
Determine collection of and tax filing requirements for Sales and Use Taxes			
Obtain appropriate licenses and permits			
Comply with zoning restrictions and requirements			
Research and understand pollution control and waste disposal restrictions			
Identify employer responsibilities			
Obtain Workers' Compensation for employees			
Obtain appropriate insurance coverage for business			
Obtain appropriate bonds			
GET SET!			
Select attorney/accountant			
Set up record keeping system			
Open business checking account			
Develop goals, functions, policies and procedures for business			
Identify product sources			
Select vendors			
Develop customer service plan and train all staff on how to interact with customers			
GO!			
Conduct a business dress rehearsal and respond to feedback from "customers"			
Develop promotional plan for startup			
Design "grand opening" or "announcement"			
Prepare press releases			

CORE FOUR® Business Planning Course

WHAT NEXT?

Take a few minutes to figure out what your next steps might be. This course has covered a lot of information and now your question is, "How do I get started?" Take a few minutes to divide your business plan into manageable pieces. The following questions were developed to help you get going. Remember, "You can do it, we can help." Fill out the following page as if it were your work plan. Let's get started…

Reference these pages as you think of topics and items that need to be completed or researched to build your business plan:

<u>MARKETING</u>:
- Table of Contents   Page i-MP
- Build Your Marketing Plan   Page 76-MP

<u>CASH FLOW PROJECTIONS</u>:
- Table of Contents   Page i-CFP
- Blank Cash Flow Projection   Page 35-CFP

<u>OPERATIONS</u>:
- Planning Checklist   Page: 32-OP

Remember, when your narrative (story) and cash flow projections are complete, and after you run your own "due diligence," you are at the point in the process where you say, "Yes, this is my dream, I want to go forward and start/expand this business." If you can't say "yes," go back to more research and modify your plan until you can. You can DO IT!

WORK PLAN OUTLINE

Date: _____   Name: _____

Phone: _____

What is your target date for completing your business plan? _____

What date would you like to start/expand your business? _____

Will your business have to meet zoning or permit requirements? _____

From the Operations Planning section, what are the top five items you need to check on?

1. _____

2. _____

3. _____

4. _____

5. _____

Which of the following areas of marketing do you need to research, and how?

1. *Customer habits, demographics, wants, and needs:*

2. *Competition. How many, where, evaluation, strengths, and weaknesses:*

3. *List your product's features and benefits:*

4. *What kinds of promotions will you need to consider?*

5. *Pricing is an art and a science. Do you need to know more to price your product/service?*

Use the worksheet on page 9 & 10 CFP to help you identify any start-up costs you need more details about:

1. _____   5. _____

2. _____   6. _____

3. _____   7. _____

4. _____   8. _____

Some of you may have done an exercise at the start of class, an executive summary. Let's go back and review it. Description of the business:

_____

_____

_____

_____

_____

_____

_____

_____

_____

_____

APPENDIX

INDEX OF WORKSHEETS

HELPFUL WEBSITE ADDRESSES

Agency	Web Address	Description
Annual Credit Report	**www.annualcreditreport.com**	Obtain a free copy of your credit report from any or all of the three major credit reporting agencies.
Bizrate.com	**www.bizrate.com**	Comprehensive list of product and pricing information on vendors.
Business Owner's Toolkit	**www.toolkit.cch.com**	Provides useful information, tips, and resources for small business owners.
Business.gov	**www.business.gov**	Federal, State, and Local laws relevant to small businesses.
City-Data	**www.city-data.com**	Profiles, photos, maps, statistics, and data about thousands of cities across the U.S.
E-Library	**www.elibrary.com**	Contains articles from newspapers, magazines, encyclopedias, and almanacs; dictionary and thesaurus entries; photo and map archives; books.
Entrepreneur.com	**www.entrepreneur.com**	Information, tips, and news about starting and growing business and business opportunities.
Federal Business Opportunities	**www.fedbizopps.gov**	A portal through which commercial vendors seeking Federal markets for their products and services can search, monitor and retrieve opportunities solicited by the entire Federal contracting community.
Federal Express	**www.fedex.com**	Website for Federal Express. Includes shipping zone and rate charts and online shipping.
Federal Trade Commission	**www.ftc.gov**	The Federal Trade Commission administers many laws pertaining to commerce and consumer relations that business owners must be aware of and abide by.
Inc. magazine	**www.inc.com**	Information from the magazine Inc.
Internal Revenue Service	**www.irs.gov**	Federal tax information and news, downloadable forms and publications. Includes a small business section with information on federal unemployment taxes, social security taxes, etc.
Internet Public Library	**www.ipl.org**	Contains information that you would find in any public library.

James J. Hill Reference Library	**www.jjhill.org**	The James J. Hill Library in Saint Paul, MN houses a world-class collection of practical business information resources and is considered one of the most comprehensive business libraries in the country.
Microsoft Small Business	**www.microsoft.com/ smallbusiness**	Sales and marketing information for small businesses.
Morebusiness.com	**www.morebusiness.com**	Informational website for small businesses.
Mysimon.com	**www.mysimon.com**	Comprehensive list of product and pricing information on vendors.
Occupational Safety and Health Administration	**www.osha.gov**	Information on safety and health standards in the workplace.
Online Women's Business Center	**http://www.sba.gov/aboutsba/ sbaprograms/onlinewbc/index. html**	Website for the Small Business Association's Office of Women's Business Ownership, which promotes the growth of women-owned businesses through programs that address business training and technical assistance, and provide access to credit and capital, federal contracts, and international trade opportunities.
Pricescan.com	**www.pricescan.com**	Comprehensive list of product and pricing information on vendors.
Sales and Marketing Executives -International	**www.smei.org**	Worldwide association of sales and marketing. The primary forum in which the world's top sales and marketing managers meet.
Small Business Association	**www.sba.gov**	Website of US Small Business Administration with many small business resources.
U.S Online Government Bookstore	**http://bookstore.gpo.gov/**	List of publications from the government printing office.
United Parcel Service	**www.ups.com**	Website for the United Parcel Service. Includes shipping zone and rate charts and online shipping.
United States Postal Service	**www.usps.com**	Website for the US Postal Service. Includes online shipping, postal service regulations, and rates.
US Citizenship and Immigration Services	**www.uscis.gov**	Includes important information for employers about employment eligibility and hiring practices among immigrant populations.

US Department of Commerce	**www.commerce.gov**	Information from and about the US Department of Commerce.
US Department of Commerce – Economic Development Administration	**www.eda.gov**	Information from and about the US Department of Commerce Economic Development Administration.
US Department of Labor	**www.dol.gov**	US Dept. of Labor website, contains employment posters, Family Medical Leave Act information, rules for breaks and overtime pay, etc. Also contains the Bureau of Labor Statistics with statistical information including the consumer price index and other useful information.
US Equal Employment Opportunity Commission	**www.eeoc.gov**	Website of the US Equal Employment Opportunity Commission, contains information on Americans with Disabilities Act, a compliance manual for discrimination, etc.
US Government Export Portal	**www.export.gov**	Information on exporting, export sales, financing exports, solving trade problems, foreign markets vs. U.S. markets, and finding a partner in the U.S.
US International Trade Administration	**www.trade.gov**	Information on markets and products, access to international markets, and competition from dumped and subsidized imports.
US Patent and Trademark Office	**www.uspto.gov**	Information on applying for and obtaining patents, trademarks, servicemarks, and copyrights.
Wall Street Journal	**www.startupjournal.com**	Small business website hosted by the Wall Street Journal – includes information and articles on businesses for sale, franchise opportunities, creating a business plan, trademark search, e-mail alerts, advice from columnists, how-to advice, ideas, franchising, financing, technology, and running a business.
Women Entrepreneurship in the 21st Century	**www.women-21.gov**	A website sponsored by the US Department of Labor and the Small Business Administration. This website offers resources, information, registration for online programs, and networking opportunities for women entrepreneurs.

Helping your business succeed

N O R T H E A S T
entrepreneur
F U N D

Northeast Entrepreneur Fund, Inc.
8355 Unity Drive, Suite 100
Virginia, MN 55792
(218) 749-4191
(800) 422-0374
www.entrepreneurfund.org
www.corefouronline.com